The Science of the Quran

Proving God's Existence through Established Modern Science

The Science of the Quran

Proving God's Existence through Established Modern Science

Ahmad Hassan

Lido Horizons Publishing

Arlington, Virginia

Lido Horizons Publishing
4201 Wilson Boulevard, Suite 110
Arlington, VA 22203
For information, please email: books@lidohorizons.com

All translations of the verses of the Quran are by the
author.

To my family—especially my parents,
and above all my mother

&

To all those who choose to boldly explore
new avenues of knowledge,
regardless of how unfathomable
they may initially appear

Contents

Preface

Writing a book about God and science in today's environment is a challenging task. Writing a book about God and science in today's environment and through the eyes of a single text (the Quran) is even more challenging. And writing such a book at a time when—primarily for geopolitical reasons—this particular text has become unpopular in many parts of the world is perhaps the most challenging. Yet writing this book, an undertaking that spanned the last six years, has proven to be one of the most mentally and spiritually enriching endeavors of my adult life.

First, the nature of the book has afforded me the opportunity to become exposed to and learn about so many interesting areas of science. This experience has in turn allowed me to gain a much deeper understanding of, and appreciation for, the sheer majesty and beauty of our world and of the larger universe we inhabit, a place we are truly fortunate to be part of. The book has also prompted and challenged me to ask some daring spiritual and philosophical questions that, after much thought and reflection, led my simple mind to realize a few things about the Truth.

I found this Truth to be quite real and also quite difficult to fully comprehend. I discovered Truth to also be quite large—so large that it simply cannot be confined in any conceivable way. The whole of Truth can never be fully captured or appreciated through any one single philosophy, religion, book, prophet, culture, people, country, civilization, time, scientific discovery, natural theory, human experience, planet, star, galaxy, or universe—or through any other single entity for that matter. I doubt if we can understand the totality of this Truth even through a combination of everything I just listed or through everything that can *ever be* listed.

Instead of capturing the sum of Truth, I have come to trust that what we continuously come across or experience represents nothing but a mere "window" into this Truth. Each and every one of these individual windows offers a unique and an especially enriching or enlightening viewpoint into that larger Truth. These windows include our sciences, philosophies, religions, spiritual practices, arts, cultures, histories, various endeavors of virtue, and, of course, our natural environment, to name just the obvious few.

Our challenge as individuals, and perhaps even as a species, then becomes to attempt to piece these various windows together, and, with any luck (or perhaps much luck), we'll gain a deeper understanding of, as well as a richer perspective into, this larger sense of Truth. And the more windows we successfully put together, the more insight we gain and the richer our understanding of this Truth hopefully becomes. We may even discover along the way how our efforts can be rewarded with something more profound—discovering how to *happily* live within Truth's grander domain.

This book represents exactly such an attempt. I aim to stitch together the truth of science with that of the Quran. In this respect, I treat the Quran as representative of religious or spiritual truth, though it represents only one particular window. More appropriately, the Quran should be seen as representing that aspect of religious or spiritual truth that promotes the notion of the existence of God, Supreme Being, or what has also been known as an intelligent and overwhelming universal order.

I wrote this book primarily for science-minded and general readers who find the notion of the existence of a supreme being to be either exciting, worthy of more study, or completely absurd. In presenting the book's material, I do not assume the reader possesses any in-depth knowledge of science, nor do I assume any prior knowledge of the Quran. I have tried my best here to explain and familiarize readers with both of these areas and have attempted—successfully, I hope—to make the reading engaging and knowledge-rich.

I do not ask anyone to presume the existence of a supreme being, nor do I ask anyone to initially accept the divine nature of the Quran. I also do not ask Muslim readers to accept, on mere faith, the particular verse interpretations I offer. Through strong, difficult-to-dismiss evidence and rational arguments, I will attempt to prove the existence of a supreme being, demonstrate the divine nature of the Quran, and argue that the verse interpretations I propose are the correct and intended interpretations, regardless of how difficult some of them may be to accept.

What I eagerly ask for, however, is that every reader come to this subject with a mental "blank sheet of paper," leaving behind any preconceptions regarding the nonexistence of a supreme being, whether a mere two-hundred-or-so-page book can *prove* the Supreme Being's existence, the nature and origin of the Quran, or what anyone thinks they "know" about the Quran's various meanings.

If this request for neutrality cannot be honored for any reason, I ask that the book be set aside until such a time that it can be honored, but I sincerely hope in such a case that the time taken to contemplate and accept neutrality is no more than a few short hours! And if by the end of your reading you remain unconvinced, then please accept my sincere gratitude for having taken the time to read the book anyway and my best wishes to you in all your future readings and life endeavors.

But if you stick with me, I promise that this experience will be attention grabbing, highly informative, thought provoking, challenging, and, if I dare say, perhaps even enlightening!

Background and Introduction

For as long as I can remember, I have always been a true admirer of science. My first science-related memory goes back to the third grade in a public school in Alexandria, Virginia. As is customary within the American public school system, the teachers asked the students to write on a small piece of paper what they wanted "to be" when they grew up. I clearly remember writing the word *scientist* on my piece of paper. However, I did not grow up to become a scientist; instead I chose electrical engineering, which has been my profession for the last twenty-three years. Nevertheless, the science "bug" never left me, and this book is, to a large extent, a reflection of that. But before going any further, it's probably worthwhile to indulge—and at times perhaps entertain—you with some personal life history, along with a few important events that shaped my early childhood and that have influenced the writing of this book.

I was born in the city of Baghdad in April of 1966. When I was about fourteen months old, my parents left Iraq and brought me to New York City. My father had just earned a scholarship to complete his higher education in America and ended up graduating with master's and doctoral degrees from New York University. We lived in New York until I was almost six years old, when my father received a job offer to work as an economist at the World Bank in Washington, D.C., so we moved to the nearby suburb of Alexandria, Virginia, where we lived for the next three years. We moved back to Baghdad in 1975, when I was about nine years old.

Culture Shock

I don't have many childhood memories, but I distinctly remember being in a state of complete shock for about the first three months after our move back to Iraq. Years later I learned that this was called culture shock. I had just been shipped to a country where I did not speak the language, nor was anything familiar, and was furthermore told that this was my new home for the indefinite future! Nevertheless, I started to accept what fate had chosen for me as a new life and began to feel more at ease as the days, weeks, and months passed by.

When we first moved to Baghdad, we lived at my grandparents' house. In Baghdad at that time, it was customary for several families to share the same house, and this was the case at my grandparents'. I did not know this curious cultural fact at the time, as my only memory up to that point was of living in an American-style apartment shared only with my parents and younger sister. During the first few days after our arrival, as I began to silently play with my cousins (I did not yet speak Arabic), I kept wondering when they would go back to where they lived. Conversely, I was worried more than anything that they would "disappear" and leave me completely alone in this new, hostile environment. However, when my mother assured me that these people actually lived in that house, just a few rooms down the hall, I was pleasantly taken aback and secretly began to thank whoever came up with the brilliant idea of sticking four families under the same roof.

The next moment of being pleasantly surprised came when I discovered that the TV stations began their daily scheduled programming at six o'clock every evening (this is hard to fathom given the continuous TV coverage we get today). After an initial fifteen-minute period of reciting the Quran, the cartoons began. Sadly, however, I also discovered that this exciting period lasted for just another fifteen-minute interval. The cartoons weren't all that bad, but because they were in Arabic, I didn't understand a single thing that was said. Nevertheless, having to choose between watching animated characters speaking a language I did not understand or staring at a dark gray TV screen with a tablecloth pulled over it (TVs were rather rare, so they needed to be protected), I definitely would have chosen the first option every time. Come to think of it, the lack of American-style cartoons was probably the biggest culture shock of all!

In the United States, I would come home from school (when I didn't miss the school bus, which was a frequent occurrence, I am told), and my mother would fix me a peanut butter and jelly sandwich. I would jump on my parents' queen-size bed and watch *real* cartoons for a good three to four hours at a time. In Baghdad, however, I had to live with just fifteen minutes of it, and I had to wait until six o'clock to do so! It was a rather difficult change for a nine-year-old to accept. Since then, I have always maintained that there ought to be an international law—adhered to by all countries—protecting nine-year-olds against such cruelty.

I began to adjust to my new environment and felt my anxiety slowly abate, but that would turn out to be short-lived, as I learned we would be moving to yet another new place. To my huge disappointment, "we" did not include everyone who lived at my grandparents' but instead involved only my immediate small family. What's more, this new place was located in a distant Baghdad suburb that didn't look anything like my grandparents' attractive upscale neighborhood, and so began episode two of the "ought to have a law against it" type of culture shock.

I think that by the time of this new move, I was becoming completely indifferent to what *normal* was. Not only was I unable to speak the language and had to wait until six o'clock to watch any children's programming, but I was also now almost completely alone. During this period, my father was teaching at the university in Baghdad and would normally leave early in the morning and would not return at night until after I was asleep. Moreover, the workweek in Iraq was six days long, which made his absence even longer. So it was me, my mother, and my sister who needed to somehow find ways to stay busy through the long and lonesome days. Though my mother did her best to keep us busy and active, she could only do so much due to the lack of things like daytime TV programming, a children's playground, good neighbors (I probably learned more bad language in these years than I have ever since then), or a decent toy store.

And when my mother wanted to take us for a walk outside the house, we had to brave 120-degree heat, unpaved roads, wandering donkeys, and feral dogs (these dogs were born wild, lived wild, looked wild, and behaved wildly toward anything or anyone who dared approach them), among other unpleasant surprises that seemed to take on a different flavor with every outing. So, we ended up staying at home a lot, which turned out to be a sort of blessing in disguise, as it had the benefit of helping me begin to learn the Arabic language I needed in order to keep up in school (the embarrassingly high number of circles around my poorer grades made my fourth-grade report card look like a subway map, with each colored circle representing a different station). Almost everything about moving to, and living at, our new home felt like a big step backward—to put it rather mildly—except for one fascinating and mind-freeing experience that would prove to have a notable and lasting effect on me.

The Everlasting Encounter

During the summer months of Baghdad, it was customary for people to sleep on the roofs of their houses. Unlike roofs on American houses, roofs on the houses of Baghdad are flat, relatively spacious, and normally made from concrete and stone tile. As soon as the sun began to set, the inhabitants would start moving mattresses, covers, pillows, blankets, food, drinks, toys, books, radios, and alarm clocks (which basically meant that *everyone* woke up when the alarm clock went off, including a few not-too-happy neighbors) to the roof area to begin "the sleeping ritual."

I call it a ritual because it was also customary for families, especially multifamily dwellings, to have dinner, chat, play, listen to music, and argue the evening away, all while being on the roof. It literally felt like going camping every night, except that this camping was not to a new frontier or a wild and faraway place—it was just to the roof. In my case, my family was pretty small, so we missed out on all the tasty feastings, lively arguments, and general good times, but we made up for it all in two very pleasant ways.

First, the area where we lived was quite far from the busiest areas of Baghdad, and during the early evening hours a cool and gentle desert breeze would begin to blow and would continue throughout the night. This breeze, in conjunction with the general calmness associated with our remoteness, felt completely different and refreshing, especially after a long hot day; it almost felt like we were in an entirely different world at night!

The second benefit came in what lay in the night sky, and this too was mainly due to the remoteness from city lights and pollution. Lying on the roof, I saw, or thought I saw, the entire universe right before my own eyes. I saw big bright stars, little faint stars, the Big and Little Dippers, and fast-moving meteors, among many curious things. I could swear that I even saw man-made satellites passing by at times! It's difficult to describe how I felt then, but anyone who's been on a summer campout in the wilderness on a clear and crisp night under the stars knows exactly what I'm describing. It was an awesome and bewildering experience that, fortunately, can never be forgotten. In my adult years, especially during the period of my research for *The Science of the Quran*, I came across authors who would confess how they were completely captivated by an outing in the wilderness. To them, seeing the night sky with all its wonder and majestic beauty created such a lasting impression that it served as a turning point for each one, the start of a new career into astronomy, cosmology, or physics. In my case, though, I had that pleasure *every night* for five or six months a year!

While gazing at the night sky, I remember asking my mother many questions, such as "What's the name of that bright star?" or "How far away is that faint star?" or "Does anyone live on that star?" She tried to answer the best she could, but I only became more and more curious as time passed by. This was when *I* got hooked on astronomy.

I missed all that when we had to spend weekends at my grandparents' house, which we did often, in their busy and older neighborhood of Baghdad. There was no cool breeze, lots of noise, lots of bugs, not many visible stars, and at times pretty heated debates. During these times, I looked forward to going back to our new home and being with my newly made friend—the night sky—again.

As I mentioned earlier, I did not speak any Arabic when my parents moved us back to Iraq. By the age of twelve, however, I was almost fluent in both speaking and writing. It's actually kind of amusing how what I lacked in Arabic, I made up for in English. And while some of my relatives would joke and laugh when I spoke or wrote Arabic (all in good spirit, of course), when it came my turn to teach them English, which was practically my first profession, I would at times find it very difficult to keep a straight face and not burst into laughter when some of them spoke, or tried to speak, English. Like I said, though, it was all in good spirit, and we enjoyed teaching and learning from each other.

Nevertheless, having a good knowledge of the English language in a foreign country had its drawbacks. I never learned—never had to learn—English grammar, even though learning English was required by the teaching curricula in Iraq (and later Jordan). I literally, to this day, know practically nothing about English grammar. I knew then how to construct sentences, not through grammar as a foreigner would learn but through being immersed in an English-only environment, having lived in the United States. I understood English well enough to pass all my tests and impress all my teachers, so there was no dire need for me to go beyond that. And certainly there was no need to struggle with learning something as dry and unexciting as grammar—a statement that's perhaps equally true for all languages. In addition, I had the gargantuan task of learning Arabic, a language more difficult and cumbersome than English in the view of many.[1]

First Introduction to the Quran

I continued to live in Baghdad until I was about fifteen years old. In 1981 my parents moved to the country of Jordan, Iraq's neighbor to the west, where my father assumed a new teaching position at the University of Jordan in Amman. By this time, however, I was completely fluent in Arabic, and it was in Jordan where I became familiar with the Quran.

I attended high school in Amman, and every school day between seven-thirty and eight o'clock in the morning, a Quranic recitation played on the school's loudspeaker. This was a completely new experience for me, as none of the schools I attended in Baghdad engaged in such a practice. The recitation was also normally done by a famous Egyptian Quranic reader by the name of Abdul-Basit, who is generally recognized as one of the most talented readers to have emerged in modern times. When Abdul-Basit read the Quran, all I wanted to do was listen. Abdul-Basit was so talented that he almost "sang" the Quran. Coupled with his beautiful voice and the linguistic richness of the Quran, I became more interested in the Quran at a time when I had begun to comprehend what the Quran was actually saying.

It was also during this three-year stay in Jordan, that I became interested in the science of physics. I hoped to pursue my passion for astronomy and

1. One of my greatest regrets in life is not having learned English grammar, because then writing this book would have been so much easier (thank God for editors).

become an astronomer when I completed my schooling, but I also started to question the practicality of finding a job as an astronomer in the Middle East at that time. With proper "help" from my parents (advice I didn't want to hear back then), I decided to give up on the astronomer idea entirely and instead pursue engineering, which I thought was somewhat related to physics and astronomy but had the added benefit of offering a good-paying job later on. Once I graduated from high school, I came back to the United States to earn my college degree. I wanted to pursue a major that combined both physics and engineering and so settled on electrical engineering (also, electrical engineers were in high demand at the time). Naturally, my relocating to America constituted yet another culture shock, but this was a *good* shock!

Deepening Interests

During my college years, I remained in touch with the Quran on a casual basis, and this remained the case until my early thirties. Throughout that period, my interest in the Quran was superficial, without any intention of seriously studying it. This changed by my midthirties, however, as I began to feel the need for spiritual growth and became interested in gaining a deeper understanding of the Quran (as well as an interest in learning more about other religions and other spiritual and philosophical ideas).

For a ten-year period after I graduated from college, my interest in science also seemed to slowly fade away, but by my midthirties I experienced a rather strong renaissance there as well. I became curious not only in topics of past interest but also in new areas that spanned a wide spectrum of science. I wanted to learn anything and everything about anything and everything that was science. I bought books, subscribed to magazines, signed up for specialized courses, and watched every science-related TV program with a great deal of interest. It was like an unexplainable but quite enriching possession that lasted for a good eight to ten years of my life.

In retrospect, it seems that the period from my midthirties to my early forties was a rather critical one (as far as writing this book is concerned), where a strong interest in learning science coincided with an equally strong interest to critically study and better understand the Quran.

Researching the Quran

There were two areas of Quranic research I was eager to explore. The first was based on a question I asked myself: If the Quran was the literal work of God, word for word, and letter for letter, as Muslims believe, then what could I learn about the nature of God beyond that portrayed through the direct language of the Quran? This was also a time when I began posing other questions, largely after becoming exposed to various scientific and

great

philosophical writings. I asked myself: What is the nature of our physical reality—our true physical reality? What is the meaning of our existence? Why is the universe so magnificent and incomprehensible? Difficult questions indeed, but ones that are better asked than not. With these questions in mind, the first area of Quranic research I pursued focused on understanding better what the notion of God really meant.

The second area of Quranic research I undertook was related to what I call the *deeper* or *hidden* Quran. It was becoming increasingly clear to me, based on several close readings, that the Quran contained another layer of meaning—a deeper one. Also at around this time, I began to explore an idea that seemed to me to be quite profound.

Every good book ever written contains a central theme or core idea that serves as the nucleus for follow-on themes and ideas the author intended to communicate. I then began to ask: Since the Quran was also a book, what was *its* core theme? Surely, the Quran, an unusual and arguably unique book and Islam's sacred text, must also contain such a core of thought as well. Answering this question and searching for this theme turned into a several-year effort, through which I discovered the Quran's central theme, along with what I believe to be its deeper layer. It seemed like this central theme or vital thought was the key that unlocked the hidden meaning of the Quran. I also discovered that at this deeper level, the Quran assumes much more clarity and consistency. It seemed as though the Quran was, in the end, all about this deeper level. Because of this discovery, I now believe that the Quran cannot be properly and meaningfully understood without an exploration of this deeper level. Absent this recognition, the Quran will probably remain the subject of various interpretations, many conflicting viewpoints, and much—and, at times, unhealthy—debate. In any event, this book is not about my research into the nature of God, nor is it about the deeper Quran. Instead, it's about the science of the Quran. But before I tell that story, I want to discuss a few verses that sparked the genesis of this book.

---

2. What is true physical reality? No one knows! A few thousand years ago, humans believed that everything was made from earth, water, air, fire, and ether. Less than three hundred years ago, humans discovered that everything was made from chemical elements. Less than two hundred years ago, humans discovered that these elements were further made from smaller atomic constituents called nuclei (which, in turn, are made from protons and neutrons) and electrons. Less than one hundred years ago, man discovered that these atomic components further break down into even more elementary entities. Where does it all end? This is the central question that true physical reality is concerned with.

Two Verses

One day during my research into the deeper meaning of the Quran, a particular verse stood out. I read and reread the verse several times. I immediately realized that the verse, although apparently somewhat cryptic, was actually talking about the future invention of a flying machine and of airplane travel. I looked at the verse again and again, until I became completely convinced that this was the actual meaning of the verse.

This was very exciting. I thought that I perhaps had been the first person to have potentially discovered the *true* meaning of a verse that no other person had yet realized. And among possibly many billions of Muslims who had ever lived, I thought that I may have been the only person who had understood what this verse was intending to communicate.

The second verse, equally surprising, was related to what scientists believe today to be the expansion of our universe. Through my study of cosmology, I had learned that our universe is expanding. In addition, the confirmation of the universe's expansion was made rather recently and only after bitter disagreements between the leading astronomers and cosmologists at the time. So, I thought, here is the Quran, a text more than thirteen hundred years old (at the time when the universe was discovered to be expanding), already pointing to this expansion.

Nevertheless, the scientific insight provided by these two verses, although quite interesting, did not constitute a large enough impetus to drive me to continue this investigation, and for a period of time I remained uncommitted to further exploration of the science of the Quran. That impetus came soon thereafter, while vacationing in the Caribbean.

The Third Set of Verses

Throughout the last seven or eight years, it has become my habit to take an annual weeklong vacation for spiritual enrichment and rediscovery. I usually use these few precious days to reflect on different things going on in my life and to plan ahead for things I felt were mostly overlooked yet quite important. During one of these trips, I found myself engrossed in a particular article concerning human evolution in the journal *Scientific American*.

Throughout my life up to that point, I had rejected the notion of evolution. Even if I could come to believe in the general idea of evolution as explaining "lower life," I could never accept its explanation of the existence of humanity. As new scientific discoveries were made and announced to the general public—such as the discovery of million-year-old human remains—I would conjure up yet another excuse for how such discoveries were completely irrelevant or might even have been fabricated. This mental disposition was due to two factors: The first was the standard interpretation of the verses of the Quran that relate to the creation of humanity, much of which was put forth prior to any recent scientific discoveries. The second came from my ignorance of the scientific advances that related to evolution.

All this drastically changed, however, on the evening I read through the *Scientific American* article. Somewhere in that reading, a light suddenly flashed in my head, and it felt as if the floodgates of "enlightenment" were opened in my mind. I confidently realized that the Quran was describing nothing but evolution when it came to the development of life in general and of the creation of humans in particular. I had memorized many of the verses that dealt with the origins of life and of humans, and it all made perfect sense to me. I concluded that the Quran does describe human evolution in agreement with science after all.

Writing This Book

This realignment in my understanding of the verses of the Quran that deal with life's origin and progress had an important secondary impact on me. I concluded that the standard interpretation of the Quran was severely flawed in several important areas. I realized that I was now free—now that I knew the truth of science was on my side—to reinterpret and rediscover the Quran, especially rediscovering the part of the Quran that contained a scientific or "natural world" component, estimated to constitute over 750 verses, or more than 12 percent of the Quran.[3] It was then that I decided to begin researching the scientific aspects of the Quran—the verses of the Quran that seemed to be supported by modern science.

My study of the science of the Quran was a gradual progression and at times quite slow. I wanted to understand the science well, and I wanted to research how other Quranic scholars had interpreted and explained some of the verses that contained a scientific component. But the more I discovered, the more I believed that something intriguing was going on with respect to the Quran and its scientific insights, as I will attempt to demonstrate throughout the rest of the book.

At some point shortly after I began this study, a key thought struck my mind—the successful demonstration of the science of the Quran would lead to potential *proof* of the existence of a supreme being. I think no other conclusion could possibly be reached that satisfactorily explains the foretelling of these kinds of scientific discoveries in a book more than fourteen hundred years old—insights that are not ambiguous, subjective, or metaphorical yet are contained in a book itself claimed to be exclusively authored by this Supreme Being.

Numerous popular science books exist today, some of which also contain

---

3. Golshani, *Quran and Sciences of Nature*, 75, 151.

a spiritual component. There have also been quite a few attempts at arguing compatibility between science and God. However, *The Science of the Quran* is unique in that I strive to prove the existence of the Supreme Being by presenting modern-day scientific insights *provided by* that Supreme Being. This overall objective also constitutes this book's central theme: The existence of this Supreme Being can now be *proven* through demonstration of the Quran's accurate foretelling of many important scientific discoveries, the majority of which have been made only in the last hundred years or so and which simply could not have been foretold by Muhammad or any other human being living fourteen hundred years ago.

This book also stands apart in several important ways from other, related Muslim scholarly works that have addressed science within the Quran: First, this book presents what I believe to be a nearly comprehensive treatment of science within the Quran. Second, although there has been prior mention in other works of some of the scientific discoveries cited in this book, the majority of the topics, in the form in which they are presented, are original to this book. Third, the interpretations I offer differ in many instances from other scholarly interpretations but are nonetheless the correct and *intended* interpretations, as I will argue and illustrate throughout. Fourth, and most importantly, I embrace the notion of evolution, where every other Quranic scholar I am aware of has not. This book would simply not have been written had it not been for my conviction that the Quran is in total agreement with evolution—a major cornerstone of modern scientific truth.

Book Overview

This book is divided into three parts. Part 1 consists of chapters 1 and 2 and introduces the Quran and the prophet Muhammad, the person responsible for delivering the Quran to humanity. I provide a somewhat detailed discussion on these two topics because I do not assume the reader to have any prior knowledge of them. Part 2 consists of chapters 3 and 4 and provides a general discussion of science, along with the important parallels between the principles of science and those of the Quran. During that discussion I argue that not only does the Quran contain established modern science but also that the Quran's very foundation aligns with the principles found in science. Part 3 consists of chapters 5 through 10 and constitutes the heart of the book, where the science of the Quran is presented and argued.

I recommend a sequential reading. I intend for the book to be concise yet information and knowledge rich, without too much discussion of extraneous topics. Because the goal of the book is to prove a profound yet elusive idea, I want readers to quickly and easily be able to judge the central theme's efficacy. I could have gone into many other areas of interest, but I've opted instead to avoid such discussions in order to prevent losing focus and "getting lost in the woods." I have, however, included a broad list of references that can be consulted to further explore topics of interest.

Notes on the Use of *Allah* and on Translations

I want to clarify a few matters prior to delving into the book. The first has to do with the term *the god*, which is used throughout the text. The Quran uses the Arabic word *Allah* for *God*. However, the word *Allah* comes from the conjoining of two other words. The first is *El*, which means "the," while the second is *ilah*, which means "god." So *Allah* in Arabic is one and the same as *the god*. The practice of combining two words into one for ease of pronunciation is quite common within the Arabic language. I also maintain the lowercase *g* for *god* in keeping with the original Arabic form.

Next, within the verses of the Quran and the sayings of the prophet Muhammad, I include two types of bracketed text. The first contains text that starts with *or*, and the words that follow represent various translations of a particular Arabic word. I do so to provide the reader with better visibility into the original word's intended meaning. The second type of bracketed text is text inserted by me to clarify context. Due to space constraints, in many instances I provide only a partial verse or set of verses. It therefore becomes important in such situations to clarify what certain words refer to, based on other parts of the verse or other adjacent verses not provided to the reader. I also opted to add the words *the god* within the verses instead of capitalizing the word that refers to God.

PART 1

Do they not carefully study the Quran? For if it was from other than the god, they would find within it many inconsistencies.

4:82

1 The Quran

The Quran is a book. Depending on page and letter size, the length of the Quran is typically between five hundred and six hundred pages.[4] The Quran is made up of chapters, and each chapter in turn is made up of a collection of verses. There are a total of 114 chapters and a little more than 6,200 verses within the Quran. The longest chapter contains 286 verses, while the shortest one contains only 3. With a few chapter exceptions, the Quran starts with the longest chapters and ends with the shortest ones, and this sequence does not correspond with when the chapters (or verses within a chapter) were revealed in time. Each chapter has its own name: "The Cow," "Mary," "The Spider," "The Table," and "The Star" are a few examples.

Muslims believe the Quran to be the *literal* work of the god. Each and every chapter, verse, and word, even down to the individual letters (it is not uncommon for an Arabic word to assume a new meaning by changing a single letter) is as was revealed by the god to the prophet Muhammad without any human addition or modification. This assertion was made by both the Quran and the prophet Muhammad and is considered to be one of the most important tenets of the Islamic faith.[5]

The Quran is an extraordinarily beautiful, eloquent, and elegant book. I fell in love with it the first time I heard select verses of it shortly after learning Arabic at the age of twelve, even though I did not fully understand what was being said. The Quran is a book that is as logical as it is emotional. It's a book that is amazingly enticing, engaging, moving, and thoughtful. The Quran makes you reflect, wonder, and imagine, and hearing the Quran makes you to want to hear more and more. It's perhaps true that no matter how many times you read or listen to the Quran, you will never grow tired of it.

---

4. The Quran has been printed on a single poster-sized sheet, but magnifying glasses are required, of course!

5. The Arabic alphabet evolved from the time just prior to the Quran's revelation to the modern Arabic alphabet, finalized about 150 years after the full revelation of the Quran. For instance, the earlier alphabet did not make use of dots, and it lacked vowel signs and the special letter *hemza*. Thus, a seventh-century Quran will look different from a Quran today.

I recently talked with my mother about the Quran. Even after I have read and listened to the Quran many times, and even after an almost seven-year period of research into it, I came across a verse and discovered a new meaning I'd never thought of before. I began to tell my mother about this new discovery. She replied that she has never read the same book nor seen the same movie twice. Yet she has read the Quran more than 120 times during her life and has never gotten tired of it.

The Quran is surprisingly easy to read and memorize. The actual Arabic word *Quran* means "to be read." Just a few years ago, I saw a child of Persian descent living in the United Kingdom who had memorized the entire Quran and who did not appear to be more than nine or ten years old. Such memorization by the young is quite common within many Muslim countries today.[6] However, memorizing the Quran and actually comprehending it are quite different things.

In spite of this ease of readability and memorization, the Quran's meaning is at times deep. For example, consider the words of Ali, a close companion to Muhammad. Ali was Muhammad's first cousin and was also practically raised by the prophet, having been adopted by him at an early age.[7] Ali once made a remark that captures the essence of the Quran: "On the surface it is elegant, yet its inside is deep. Its surprises never cease, and its mysteries never end. And it leads its readers to none other than enlightenment (leading to the next life)."[8]

The Origin of the Quran

The Quran came to us through the prophet Muhammad in the form of a revelation that lasted for a period of about twenty-three years between 610 and 632 CE. This revelation took place between the angel Jubraeel (the biblical archangel Gabriel) and Muhammad. At times, Gabriel would physically appear to Muhammad in the form of a white-clothed man and reveal verses to Muhammad, while at other times the revelation would not be a physical one. It's believed that the complete Quran was memorized and written down but not compiled in its current form during the lifetime of the prophet. The Quran contains more than thirty verses that specifically state the Quran to be the direct sole authorship of the god, and one of these

---

6. Although difficult to believe, the Quran has been memorized in its entirety by many who do not even speak Arabic!

7. Throughout this book, "the prophet" should be understood to refer to Muhammad.

8. El-Amidi El-Tamimi, *Hikkem El-Imam Ali Alaiyhee El-Salam*, saying 1547. Also see sayings 1775, 4932, 8028, 10527, 10528, 10530, 10533, 10534, and 10535.

verses also states that the Quran was, and is, under "the god's protection (or preservation)" against change and for all time.[9]

The Importance of the Quran

Muslims believe the Quran to be *the* miracle of the prophet Muhammad. Before I attempt to explain this, though, I'll need to provide some useful background.

According to traditional Islamic belief, the god never sends (or tasks) a prophet to the general human population without accompanying that prophet with one or more miracles that prove the prophet to be a person coming on behalf of the god to provide humanity with a set of instructions or special guidance. For example, according to the Quran, the prophet Moses was accompanied by a number of miracles, including a cane that turned into a snake, splitting the sea into two giant mountains, and a bright white hand. The prophet Jesus, too, was accompanied by a set of extraordinary miracles that included healing the sick, raising the dead, and conversing with others while still a mere infant. More miracles are reported in the Quran and attributed to other prophets as well.

In the case of the last prophet, Muhammad, the main miracle was the Quran. In addition to the miracle of the Quran, the prophet was reported to have demonstrated other miracles, such as curing a sickly sheep, healing a young handicapped boy, and talking with the dead. However, the miracle of the Quran is special above all others because it is a book, a miracle that can be demonstrated over and over again to anyone living away and apart from where and when other miracles might have taken place. The miracle of the Quran is therefore understood to be a living and eternal miracle.

Why a Book?

To emphasize this point, we can now ask a rather simple but essential question: Why must the miracle of the last prophet be in the form of a book? The answer, I think, is rather logical and straightforward as I'll explain, but again, I'll need to provide some useful religious and historical context.

Sometime probably between forty-five and fifty-five hundred years ago in what is now Iraq lived a man named Ibraheem (the biblical Abraham). Abraham, as told by the Quran, appeared to be a young man who may have also been part of the power class within his society. Abraham was a thoughtful individual who questioned the religious practices of his environment. He was clearly in search of the god but had nowhere to start from except the power of his own mind.

---

9. 15:9

Abraham somehow understood and accepted the existence of one su- preme being, but he did not know what or who that supreme being was. And so, after initially thinking that the Supreme Being was in the form of grand things around him, such as the sun or moon, he realized during what must have been a moment of incredible insight, that the Supreme Being was something or someone that completely transcended his immediate and known reality. It's quite astonishing how sometimes rethinking or reexam- ining a familiar, everyday issue or problem in a new way can yield a flood of new insight and knowledge. Such enlightenment has been witnessed and reported by many scientists and common people alike when discovering something new or when solving a seemingly insurmountable problem.[10]

This flood of fresh knowledge must have elevated Abraham to a com- pletely new state that redefined his very being with a renewed sense of vigor and excitement. He began to immediately share his newfound knowledge with his people, but that unfortunately was to no avail. It must have been particularly disappointing to Abraham that even his own father could not accept Abraham's new insight. Abraham thus realized that nothing short of a bold "experiment" was needed to grab his people's attention and get them to start listening. He then grabbed a blunt hard object and began breaking apart all the statutes his people were known to worship. He left only one—the most revered one—standing. When his people walked into their temple, they were completely shocked by what they saw and realized that none other than Abraham could have done such a thing, so they brought him forth to confess and explain what happened. When confronted, however, Abraham cleverly asked, "Why don't you ask them [the statues Abraham destroyed] and have them tell you?" To which they angrily replied, "But they do not speak!" Abraham countered, "And you worship and submit your life affairs to things that do not speak or hear? Do you not realize this!"

It was a daring and sincere attempt by Abraham to help his people realize the error of their ways, but instead of being appreciated as a caring adviser, he was quickly denounced as a blasphemous enemy. The events that followed, which I won't get into here, have defined the spiritual and religious context for billions of Jews, Christians, and Muslims ever since. From a particular perspective, Abraham was welcomed by the Supreme Being (or the god) and was given a new homeland and progeny. What

---

10. This experience is portrayed in the story behind "Eureka!" when Archimedes leaped out of his bathtub and ran naked through the streets of Syracuse after real- izing that the volume of water displaced by his body was equal to the volume of his submersed body, a significant insight that led to the ability to compute volumes of complex shapes in a completely new and accurate way.

Abraham gave up in search of Truth, the god made up for by establishing, from Abraham, a line of prophets who would later complete Abraham's mission to humanity. This line of prophets, according to the Quran, started with Adam, the first prophet to humanity, continued through the prophet Noah, and then went on to Abraham, with many other prophets occurring between these three major figures. At the prophet Abraham, however, an important split occurred.

Abraham had two sons who are also considered prophets: the elder Ismaeel (the biblical Ishmael) and Is'haq[11] (the biblical Isaac). From Isaac's line came monotheistic prophets including Moses, King David, King Solomon, and Jesus, among many others mentioned in the Quran as well as in the Old and New Testaments. From Ishmael's line came only one prophet, however: the prophet Muhammad. And this prophet would be the last prophet, or what's also known as the "seal" of Abrahamic prophets. Both the Quran as well as the prophet himself asserted that Muhammad was the final prophet from the line of Abraham, an assertion we'll further explore in the next chapter. The last prophet thus followed a long line of prior monotheistic prophets, which numbered more than one hundred thousand, according to common Muslim religious tradition.

If we can subscribe to this general account, then it makes sense for the miracle of the last prophet to be something that can be demonstrated(?) anywhere and at any time after the passing of that prophet. And it can probably be argued that nothing better than a book can serve this purpose. The book—if shown to remain unchanged from the time of its direct revelation—effectively becomes somewhat of a timeless miracle, and this is what Muslims believe the Quran to be.

Why Arabic?

I think this is a somewhat more complex question, but I'll endeavor to provide a plausible explanation.[12] To better understand the answer I offer (and by no means am I the first to offer it), we'll need to take a mental trip back in time to the social conditions that prevailed within the Arabian Peninsula during the sixth century CE.

During this period, the Arabs were known to possess a multitude of superior linguistic abilities, including those required for constructing great works of prose and poetry. Some of the linguists of this period possessed extraordinary qualifications and skills. These skills were publicly

---

11. The apostrophe is meant to signify a momentary pause.
12. Clearly, if Muhammad was chosen or predestined to become the last prophet, then Arabic was a natural choice since it was the prophet's language, but there's more to explore here, as we'll see.

demonstrated during frequent competitions in which linguists "dueled" for hours on end until an apparent victor was declared. During these competitions, which probably received the same level of crowd enthusiasm as the gladiators received during Roman times, competing linguists were required to construct their works on the spot with little or no prior preparation. In addition, "classical" Arabic poetry, the common form of poetry of the day, was a complex and difficult undertaking that required every verse to rhyme with the previous and following verses. On the other hand, free verse poetry, similar to that of English poetry today, as well as to much modern Arabic poetry, is mostly free from these limitations. Classical Arabic poetry thus possessed a level of complexity and intricacy that severely restricted qualification to becoming a "linguistic master." I strongly suspect that Arabs actually "bred" for these linguistic skills, as they brought great fame and fortune to anyone who possessed them. Muhammad himself, however, was illiterate prior to and after his mission, and he was known to have disliked poetry, especially the poetry of the Arabs of this period, in which much undeserved praise went toward idols and tribal chiefs.

It's not an exaggeration then to state that this period was the golden age of Arabic prose, poetry, and language in general, and it was into this highly charged and rich linguistic environment that the Quran was revealed. In essence, the Quran came as a challenge to the Arabs, and several verses within the Quran specifically embody this challenge. Within these verses, the Quran states that if anyone can come up with anything like the Quran or with smaller parts of it, down to an individual chapter, then let them do so, and let the challenge be a public one, with those present attesting a victor.[13] In another verse (17:88), the Quran states that if all of humanity were to "put their heads together" to come up with something like the Quran, they will surely fail to do so. The Quran further states that if no one can meet this challenge, then they should accept the Quran to be the sole authorship of the god.

It's not that the Arabs haven't tried to see the challenge of the Quran, but apparently such challenges were always met with failure. For a period of time after the initial revelation of the Quran, the prophet Muhammad earned the nickname "the magician,"[14] because several linguistic masters sent by the Arab chiefs to challenge Muhammad and the Quran, upon realizing the futility of their challenge, proclaimed, "By God, this is not the work of a man!" The new faith gained quite a few early converts through this endeavor, and the challenge of the Quran has remained plain since its revelation and is believed to have remained unmet to the present day.

13. 2:23 and 10:38

14. 38:4

Surely an indicator of v. high I Q.

In essence, if you can't come up w/ a better explanation of God.

What Is the Quran About?

The Quran contains a number of major themes. The first theme, a quite substantial one, describes the god. The respective verses within this theme attempt to place bounds on what the god is and what the god is not in terms of general qualities, attributes, or ways. I estimate almost 20 percent of the Quran to lie within this theme. Some of these descriptions are direct and easy to understand, while others are more subtle. Also, much of this description is similar to that of prior descriptions contained within prior scripture, while others are different.

The second theme comprises a set of beliefs, with the most important belief being the existence of the god. Other beliefs include the belief in life after death, belief in a place called Heaven (as well as the complementary Hell), belief in prior prophets such as Moses and Jesus, and belief in prior divine books such as the Torah and the Bible. Further beliefs include the belief in the equality of man and woman, as well as the equality of all races in the eyes of the god. One of the most important elements of this belief system is the belief in the merit of goodness or *virtue*. So many verses in the Quran describe how it does not matter to the god how, or how frequently, a person conducts certain acts of worship, such as prayer, fasting, or pilgrimage, if the core sense of virtue is weak or nonexistent in that person. The Quran even talks of how the notion of religion itself is secondary to that of virtue.

The third theme strives to establish a certain code of conduct or a behavioral system. This includes acts of behavior within the family, within a community, between and among members of various religions, and within the general framework of humanity. Within this theme, the Quran stresses notions such as the importance of compassion, love, respect, generosity, the avoidance of hatred and anger, living happily but responsibly, recognizing and fighting tyranny, fairness, equality, and moderation.

The fourth theme is what can be best described as "learning from the past." Within this theme, the Quran describes many past events and circumstances, with the hope that those reading the Quran will glean certain useful lessons from them. The Quran usually has a special way of telling a particular story. These stories generally provide pointed and concise accounts that may also be repeated with similar or different details in several places in the Quran. These stories are quite engaging and at times literally transport the reader to a particular place, time, or circumstance. I will provide more details on the stories of the Quran later in this chapter.

The fifth theme deals with the meaning and significance of the existence of life in general and of humanity's existence in particular. Also within this theme, the Quran tries to provide the reader with a sense of "what's to come" after death.

major theme of the Quran is what I summarize in this book: an
ding of the natural world—aka the science of the Quran. And
, in my judgment, constitutes an important component of the
s nature of the Quran.

The Quran's Concept of Haqq

The Quran contains and attempts to explain many important concepts, such
as the concepts of the god, life, death, virtue, resurrection, and the afterlife.
One of the most important of these concepts is called *Haqq* (Arabic for
"truth, fair, right, proper, or correct").[15]

The concept of Haqq is one of the paramount concepts of the Quran,
second only to that of the existence of the god, in my view. In fact, the
concept of Haqq is so important that, in several places within the Quran,
its significance is placed *above* that of the god. Because of its significance,
I keep the original Arabic word without translation throughout the book,
because I believe Haqq to be a complex concept that is best used "as is"
and not translated into any other word of lesser meaning or expression.

It's been proposed within certain scholarly circles that the concepts of
Haqq and the god are one and the same and that one does not exist in the
absence of the other. While I believe this perspective to hold merit, I perceive the concept of Haqq to be different from that of the god, especially
since the Quran has deemed such differentiation necessary in the verses
where the concept of Haqq is given more importance than that of the god.
So what exactly can I say about this vital concept?[16]

First, Haqq entails certain things. Most importantly, neither the universe, nor life, nor humanity would be here without Haqq. Haqq seems to
be the foundation on which we came to be. Or, expressed differently and
according to the Quran, Haqq was a precondition for our very existence.
Next, Haqq sets bounds or limits on what can or cannot happen within
the realm of our reality or existence. In this respect, it's like a natural law.
It cannot be violated, and it sets rules and pathways that must be duly followed and adhered to.

Haqq also implies the existence of a delicate balance within the universe
in general and within life in particular. When disturbed, an attempt is

---

15. Although difficult for an English-speaking person to pronounce, Haqq may be
best pronounced by conjoining the bolded parts of "**ha**t" and "**duck**."

16. At times, I speak of the Quran as if it is a sentient being. This may strike some
as odd since the Quran is a book. However, because it is so engaging and captivating and because of its reason-based back-and-forth delivery of its messages,
the Quran does in fact *seem* as a sentient being to an astute Arabic reader. This
perspective will become clearer as we continue through the book and meet many
verses that support this view.

made—through Haqq—to restore balance. A good example that perhaps demonstrates this sense of balance may be our current global-warming problem. We are all too familiar with the well-publicized negative consequences that global warming is predicted to have on our planet. Many scientists have argued that these negative consequences have taken place because humans disturbed a delicate balance within our atmospheric environment as a result of many years of unchecked levels of harmful emissions (more on this topic in chapter 6). The concept of Haqq also entails a strict sense of accountability and "cosmic justice." According to Haqq, positive actions meet positive ends while negative actions are likewise met with less fortunate ends. And finally, Haqq embodies a measure of purpose and direction for everything and communicates reverence, purity, and beauty inherent within all.

Is the Quran "Lost" When Translated?

This is an important question that has come up frequently throughout the Quran's fourteen-hundred-year history. Some have proposed that once the Quran is translated, it loses its significance and becomes just another ordinary book. In effect, it's no longer "the Quran" and therefore is not the timeless miracle it's claimed to be. While this may be true on the surface, there are nonetheless several points worth pondering before drawing such a conclusion.

First, the themes of the Quran mentioned in a previous section are not lost during the act of translation. A reader of a well-translated Quran will gain just as much understanding of these themes as an Arabic reader would from reading the original text. The themes that outline the description of the god, the belief system, the moral environment, the lessons of the past, and the themes that relate to important spiritual and philosophical issues are well preserved when translating the Quran. Furthermore, the arguments and reasoning used by the Quran to help readers understand and accept its important messages are all preserved as well. Also upheld is the scientific aspect of the Quran as proposed in this book, which, as I stated earlier, constitutes an important component of the miraculous nature of the Quran.

What *is* lost during the act of translation, however, is the linguistic beauty and absolute eloquence of the Arabic Quran, and this loss is, unfortunately, quite substantial. It seems that a translated Quran is simply not "the Quran" anymore. In fact, when I read the Arabic Quran and then read an English version, I cannot say they represent the same reading experience—far from it.

In my earlier years, I had the opportunity to read both Charles Dickens and Ernest Hemingway in English and Arabic versions. And even though this was a while back (more than I care to think about), I don't recall perceiving a huge difference between the two linguistic versions for either author, in that both seemed to me at the time to be beautiful works of prose.

This is not the case with the Quran. For me, reading the Quran in Arabic and then in English represent two distinct experiences. If I can provide a rather crude example, imagine watching the movie *Avatar* in 3D at the theater when it was first released (an experience I'll probably never forget) and then watching it at home some time later on a twenty-year-old, 20-inch color TV set. Although the movie is the same, the individual experiences are vastly different.

So what does this all mean? I honestly don't know if we can draw a firm conclusion one way or the other on whether or not the Quran is lost or preserved during the act of translation. However, if you ever wanted to explore the real Quran experience, I would strongly recommend you consider signing up for an Arabic language course. It will most likely be a long and steep climb, but it is surely worth it in the end!

The Quran vs. Islam

Let's next explore the differences between the Quran and the religion of Islam. I want to discuss this because of a general tendency within popular culture today to indiscriminately lump the two without a clear understanding of what each is concerned with. And while the Quran is tightly related to Islam, proper separation between the two should (or must) be recognized. They are, after all, two rather independent and distinct entities.

As noted earlier, the Quran is seen as encompassing the "pure" and direct revelation from the god to the prophet Muhammad. As such, the Quran is understood to be the holy book of Muslims, just like the Bible is that of Christians. In my view, however, the Quran cannot be so restricted. If the premise regarding the divine and direct nature of the Quran is accepted, then it follows that the Quran can be argued to be the only text within human hands today that constitutes the pure and direct message from the god, free from any human influence (or change)—an assertion that cannot be made for other religious or spiritual texts today, at least none that I'm aware of. This clearly sets the Quran apart. More importantly, it becomes a book that needs to be studied and understood by all. In spite of this importance, the Quran should not be perceived as a text that replaces other texts but as one that can further their understanding. This statement is also true for the Quran to a certain extent, in that I do not believe the Quran itself can be completely understood without an understanding of other texts as well. Within my own experience, one of the reasons why I think I may have gained a good understanding of the Quran is because of my exposure to, and candid interest in, other faiths and texts, both within as well as outside of traditional monotheism. I would not have been able to gain the understanding of the Quran I have today through a strictly Quran-only perspective.

The assertion concerning how the Quran came to be free from human influence is an important one that needs to be briefly touched on. Although I will not get into the details of how the Quran we have today came to be the one and only Quran (remember that the Quran was memorized but not compiled in its present form when the prophet lived), I can state a few well-accepted historical facts that relate to this issue. First, the Quran is believed to have been committed to memory by the prophet Muhammad, as well as by a relatively large number of companions, who numbered in the scores, or even hundreds, of individuals. The Quran was also written to various media by select scribes (Ali was one of the prophet's scribes), and the prophet himself dictated the Quran's sequence of chapters and their respective verse sequences.

All of these acts and instructions are believed to have taken place during the lifetime of the prophet. However, it is also well accepted that a single complete copy of the Quran bearing "the seal of the prophet" did not exist prior to his death. What is accepted by virtually all Quranic historians is that shortly following the death of the prophet, within less than twenty to thirty years, a process of "gathering" and collecting the Quran was initiated. This process was based on a majority rule and yielded a single agreed-upon copy of the Quran, believed to have been the "original" Quran and which is also believed to have remained unchanged to our present day.

It has also been claimed by some historians that Ali collected and maintained a complete copy of the Quran at the time of the prophet's death or soon thereafter.[17] With regard to Ali, I have spent a good amount of time studying his teachings and life philosophy apart from this book or any other previously mentioned area of research. And based on what I have learned about Ali's closeness to the prophet as well as his almost unbelievably scholarly nature, I believe that Ali would have surely maintained a complete copy of the Quran even prior to the prophet's death. Recognizing Ali's inquisitive and learned personality, the prophet reportedly once said, "I am the city of knowledge, and Ali is its gate."

---

17. Historians generally agree that Ali secluded himself immediately following the death of the prophet and did so most likely to compile the Quran. However, some historians have claimed that Ali's version differed in some verse sequences (at a minimum) from the later Quran. This account has been generally discounted, though, because Ali approved the "other" Quran and did not attempt to replace it with his own version (the existence of which has never been proven and is generally disbelieved) when he became the fourth Islamic ruler some decades after the prophet's death.

We must also perhaps recognize that the Quran, being the book of God, was in all likelihood seen as a big deal by the majority of early Muslims and thus must have been preserved and protected accordingly. This assumption is perhaps similar to how we assume the Founding Fathers of America preserved and protected the original Declaration of Independence, given its obvious significance.

Nevertheless, the issue of whether or not the Quran was subject to change since its first revelation is probably going to remain a topic of some debate, but this should not, in any way, be looked on as threatening the arguments I make in support of this book's central theme. In other words, we cannot suggest that Muhammad, or any other purely human influence living fourteen hundred years ago, could have written the verses that embody the kind of scientific insights I present in Part 3.

Let's now turn to Islam.

Islam, as most of you already know, is a religion that adheres to a certain set of beliefs, norms, and practices. Because of its original place in geography and its relatively recent appearance, the Islamic religion has also been subject to broad cultural and ethnic influences over its fourteen-hundred-year history. Many of these influences have generally played a positive role in advancing the values of the Quran and the cause of Islam, while others have been rather negative and, in certain circumstances, quite harmful. One of the most severe challenges I believe Islam has struggled with, and continues to struggle with, is the culture of tribalism.

The influence of the tribal way of life is perhaps to be somewhat expected, since the Quran was initially revealed into a tribal society and because most Muslim countries today have been, for the most part, influenced by a strong tribal cultural tide. What I have found surprising, though, is how difficult it has been for such tribal influence to lessen its grip even following many centuries of human change and progress. For instance, within many Arab, as well as perhaps many Muslim, countries today, tribal norms and ways drive societal and cultural behavior just as they did more than two thousand years ago. In this sense, not much general cultural progress has been achieved within many of these societies, even with the advent and embracing of Islam. In many respects, both the Quran and the prophet Muhammad have attempted to address and correct many negative tribal norms but have thus far been unable to realize much progress. I do not provide an extensive discussion of this here, since it does not directly relate to the core subject of the book, but I can provide two supporting examples.

The first relates to the status of women within many Muslim societies today. As I'll discuss in the next chapter, both the Quran and Muhammad were instrumental in allowing women rights and privileges that were completely denied them prior to the revelation of the Quran and the advent of Muhammad. Beyond that, Muhammad elevated the general status of women through many of his teachings by emphasizing their right to education and self-sustenance (work) as well as their active participation in various matters of importance within society. Today, however, due to the strong tribal influence noted earlier, women in certain Islamic societies are generally perceived to be repressed second-class citizens, subject to constant male and societal exploitation.

The second example relates to the assumption and passing of rule (as in power of governance) within current and past Islamic governments. Ever since the death of the prophet, the overwhelming majority of Islamic rulers have attempted to wield influence in a manner similar to how a tribal leader assumes power. You can argue that such behavior (and attitude) clearly went against the spirit of the Quran, as well as against the objective of Islam, a new religion that was envisioned to become plural and equal and be based on the merit of virtue (virtue in this case meaning that the most *qualified* individual should be granted power of rule). Of all the negative influences on the Islamic religion, the aspect of how utterly incompetent and self-serving rulers have risen to power—and the general state of misery they created—has been severely incapacitating to Muslims as well as to the appropriate development of the Islamic faith itself. It's also unfortunate that this cycle seems to be unbreakable even to the present day and equally unfortunate that the general teaching of young Muslims is (and has been) such that these values, along with many other negative tribal values, represent "proper Islam."

I don't mean to paint an overly pessimistic picture of this issue here, as there are clearly many positive tribal norms that have helped promote the teachings and values of the Quran or that are positive norms and behaviors in and of themselves. However, the overall effect of the tribal way of life has been mostly harmful on many past and present Muslim societies. More seriously, though, the generally toxic tribal environment has been at times strongly reflected in the general interpretation and understanding of the Quran, as I'll discuss in more detail later. Thus, Islam has been subjected to a number of influences, and the combination of all influences—good and bad—has defined the Islamic religion we have today, similar to how any other religion has been defined by its own set of political, cultural, and ethnic influences over hundreds or even thousands of years.

Another useful way to look at the difference between the Quran and Islam is through the act of interpreting the Quran. Much of what Islam is, or what Islam *should be*, actually comes from the Quran. However, interpreting the Quran is ambiguous and somewhat daunting at times, as we'll later discover. "What does this verse mean exactly?" is a question that continues to challenge many Islamic scholars and ordinary Muslims alike. Muslims have relied on religious authorities to help interpret certain parts of the Quran, of course, but there are also important differences among these authorities. Thus, the acts of *interpreting* the Quran (whether correctly done or not) and *applying* the Quran (also whether correctly done or not) have attempted and continue to attempt to "transform" the Quran into Islam.

Islam vs. the Concept of Islam

In addition to the distinction between the Quran and Islam, another important distinction needs to be made between Islam and what I call the Quran's "concept of Islam." I will note here, though, that the concept of Islam is a new term that, to my knowledge, has not previously been proposed within any other Islamic scholarly work. Since I am not and do not consider myself to be a scholar of the Islamic faith, other Muslims may find drawing such a distinction to be inaccurate and perhaps even unnecessary. It is, nonetheless, a point that at the very least should be entertained.

Both Islam and the concept of Islam are referred to by the same word within the Quran, but they reflect two rather separate and distinct meanings. As stated earlier, Islam (the religion) encompasses a set of acts and beliefs, of which five are considered the most important: the five daily prayers, giving charity to those in need, fasting between sunrise and sunset during the month of Ramadan, performing a once-in-a-lifetime pilgrimage to Mecca if a person is financially and physically able, and believing in the existence of the god and that Muhammad is one of his prophets. Because they constitute the heart of the Islamic faith, these five acts and beliefs are normally referred to as the "pillars of Islam" and, to a great extent, also embody what the Islamic faith is all about. The Quran's concept of Islam, however, is something different.

Within many verses in the Quran, this concept is mentioned when, for example, discussing past prophets (prior to Muhammad) while associating the word *Islam* with them. Clearly, these prophets were not Muslims in the modern definition of a Muslim, as it's not known whether many of them even visited Mecca, as is required of Muslims today. Also, we cannot assume that the methods of praying and fasting practiced by these prophets were exactly the same as the methods practiced by Muslims today. Yet, they are sometimes still referred to as "Muslims" within the Quran.

When I study this new concept of Islam, I walk away with the understanding that it is a more fundamental, simpler, and purer state of being, the essence of which is to live in total virtue and be in a state of complete peace and harmony with the god. I thus see the concept of Islam as perhaps being parallel to that of the concept of self-actualization known within the field of psychology. Self-actualization is usually defined as the final level of psychological development that can be achieved after all basic physical needs, such as those of safety and health, and all mental needs, such as those of emotional stability and proper self-awareness, have been fulfilled. It's a state to strive to and, when realized, provides a person with meaning, purpose, and fulfillment. In a similar fashion, the concept of Islam is also a state to strive to and can be attained only after much learning and self-development.

It can thus be said that not every Muslim can realize the concept of Islam; likewise, not every person who possesses the concept of Islam is a Muslim. As a matter of fact, when I look at the lives and missions of the great contemporary humanitarian leaders of the world, such as those of Mahatma Gandhi, Mother Teresa, and His Holiness the Dalai Lama, among many others, I cannot help but conclude that all these individuals qualify for, and attained, the Quran's concept of Islam, although they clearly are not Muslim.

The Quran's notion of using a particular word to mean two somewhat different things is common. Within this book, for example, I explain how the word *sky* used in the Quran can in one instance mean "airplane" and in another mean "the universe," in addition to its general meaning of "the sky." Another important example of the Quran's reuse of the same word to denote rather different things concerns the word that's been commonly translated as "infidel" and popularized within our global culture today. There are actually five distinct and separate meanings of the original Arabic word that is generally translated as "infidel" within the Quran (the word also translates to "farmer," and this meaning is in addition to the five). Ignorance of these multiple meanings has led many to assign the original Arabic word a single translation and a meaning that corresponds with being "non-Muslim." You may be wondering why the Quran does not spell things out more precisely and clearly. My sincere hope is that a partial answer to this question will be realized once you read through the rest of the book and gain a better understanding of the nature, as well as perhaps the deeper *intent*, of the Quran.[18]

Stories of the Quran

As was stated earlier in this chapter, one of the prevalent themes in the Quran is learning from the past. The Quran accomplishes this learning through its various beautifully told stories of past places, people, practices, and mindsets. Each of these accounts then brings up a certain aspect of life,

---

18. In the case of the "concept of Islam," though, because the Arabic word *Islam* means "peaceful submission," we can see why the Quran reused this word. This points to another important aspect of the Quran: the Quran wants its readers to sometimes think beyond the surface meaning of a word (in this case, being Muslim) and explore its deeper, intended meaning (living "in peace").

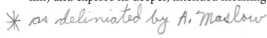
* as deliniated by A. Maslow

culture, or behavior to teach a particular lesson or emphasize an important message. However, the Quran does not necessarily specifically state what particular lesson or wisdom we need to walk away with from any particular story. This is somewhat to be expected since the Quran emphasizes the acts of thinking and careful study in many verses, as we'll explore in more detail in chapter 4. The Quran therefore *wants* those who are observant and reflective to benefit more from these stories than those who choose to read at a surface level.

One of the most prominent stories within the Quran is that of the prophet Moses—in my mind the most important character of the Quran— and the associated events that were witnessed by this prophet. The Quran tells of the adoption of baby Moses by the pharaohs, how Moses came to be a prophet, the challenges endured against the pharaoh, and the story of the Exodus into a promised land after splitting a sea into two giant mountains. The Quran also discusses the story of the biblical Mary, mother of Jesus. Mary is depicted by the Quran as a saintly young woman who possesses a supreme sense of virtue. The Quran describes how she—while still a virgin—gives birth to a baby boy who can perform an array of miracles, even as a mere infant. The Quran also mentions the stories of the prophets Adam, Noah, and Abraham, among others.

One of the most elaborate and beautifully told stories by the Quran is that of the prophet Ya'qoob (the biblical Jacob) and his sons, the most important being the prophet Yusuf (the biblical Joseph). Yusuf is also the title of the chapter in which this story is told. It's a story of love, envy, struggle, and forgiveness and of overcoming extreme difficulty through patience, hope, and faith. Almost every time I read or hear a recitation of this story, I learn something new about our humanity and what the goals of life should really be. It's amazing how, in the end, much of the human condition is perhaps accurately captured and communicated by the Quran in the story of the prophet Joseph, his father, and his siblings. It's no wonder then why the Quran starts this story by stating, "There are many useful lessons to be learned by the curious [or the asking], in the story of Joseph and his siblings."[19]

Addressing Negative Perceptions

In recent times, especially during the years following the events of September 11, 2001, the Quran has become a topic of considerable discussion, such as whether it contains verses that may be interpreted as being hostile to

---

19. No chapter better illustrates the sheer linguistic beauty of the Quran as does the chapter of Yusuf. Because this chapter is a fifteen- to twenty-page historical narrative, you might expect it to become disengaging at some point. Not only is this not the case, but readers are generally drawn to read or hear the chapter repeatedly!

non-Muslims, with some people going as far as saying that these verses are the reason why some "Muslims" have resorted to pursuing acts of hatred and violence against others.

I think that part of this attitude toward the Quran stems from the— correct—perception that the Quran is not a straightforward book to interpret.[20] The other part, however, lies in the somewhat general state of ignorance as to what the Quran is all about. In this section of the chapter, I will briefly address some of the general criticisms that have been specifically attributed to the Quran in the hope that thoughtful exploration of these criticisms will further our understanding of the Quran.

First, to speak to the point that the Quran contains verses that are critical toward non-Muslims, I believe, based on a significant amount of research into the Quran, that the Quran is more critical of Muslims than it is of non-Muslims. Some may find this somewhat surprising, but I believe it to be true. Second, it can be argued that the Quran is a book concerned with one paramount goal: the *preservation* of virtue. This preservation is what I believe is the essence of the Quran and the metric by which the Quran judges different individuals, groups, societies, cultures, and even religions— all religions, including the Islamic one (remember that the Quran and Islam are not one and the same, or, more appropriately, Islam does not "speak for" the Quran). In seeking the merit of virtue, the Quran states:

> *And we [the god] have made you [humanity] different tribes*
> *and peoples so that you know [or befriend] each other. Surely,*
> *the best among you in the eyes of the god are the most virtuous.*
> (49:13)

So the primary concern of the Quran must be understood to be the preservation of virtue, a concern that is sometimes taken to some rather strange extremes, as the following story illustrates.

During the early period following the initial revelation of the Quran to the prophet, Muhammad expended a significant amount of time and effort talking to different people about the new message but also realized that ordinary people ultimately followed their leaders and elders. To effect any real change, Muhammad understood that he needed the belief and acceptance of the well-respected and powerful individuals of society. On one particular day, Muhammad was deep in conversation with several of these tribal leaders (who generally remained adamantly opposed to Muhammad in favor of their idols, as we will talk about in greater detail

---

20. One of the reasons why the Quran is difficult to interpret at times is precisely because it is not a shallow or one-dimensional book.

in the next chapter) when an old blind man showed up, eagerly wanting to meet the new prophet and hear firsthand what he had to say. This blind man had trekked from a nearby town, where he had heard of a new message being delivered by a final prophet in Mecca.

However, because he was preoccupied with his back-and-forth discussions with the tribal leaders, Muhammad shunned the old man, and the following verses were immediately revealed (to Muhammad):

> *He [Muhammad] frowned and turned his back when the blind one came. And how would you [Muhammad] know, for perhaps he wants purity. Or he wants to seek knowledge and this knowledge will help him. But he [the tribal chief] who does not seek such knowledge, you are fully engaged with. And it is not your concern [or obligation] that he [the tribal chief] does not seek [or appreciate, want] this knowledge. But for he [the blind one] who comes to you in excitement [or love] and he is thoughtful [of the god], you are distracted. No! This [the Quran] is but a reminder, for those who wish [or want] to be reminded [or seek knowledge].*
>
> (80:1–12)

Following this incident, every time Muhammad saw this old man again, he would smile; give him a warm hug; and, after seating the man beside him, would say, "Warm greetings and blessings to the one through whom my life giver has gently disciplined!" A gracious and kind response indeed, unforthcoming from the majority of us in a similar situation, but one that reflects on the last prophet's unusually virtuous character, which we'll further explore in greater depth in the next chapter.

Now, you may ask: Couldn't the Quran have forgotten about the prophet's behavior during this incident and just let the matter go? Muhammad was, after all, the prophet of a new religion, the last prophet, and the only individual through whom the entirety of the Quran was brought forth to humanity! Clearly, the Quran did not feel that such disregard could be justified, probably because, in that single moment, virtue had been violated. Also, because the Quran is "a book of Haqq" (as the Quran sometimes refers to itself), this violation had to be called out and properly addressed, even if it came from Muhammad himself.

So, if the Quran called out its own prophet, would it not call out others when the merit of virtue was violated? To a large extent, this is the case with many of the verses that may seem critical of both non-Muslims and, as I stated earlier, Muslims. One point I need to clarify, though, is that the Quran never takes a position against the whole of any religion. What the

Quran criticizes and attempts to correct are certain beliefs or behaviors that, in the eyes of the Quran, have deviated from the true and intended *way of the god* or that stand in the way of embracing the main message of the Quran.[21] Also, when the Quran raises a particular issue, it almost always substantiates and explains both its stated position and why it chooses to raise that issue. During such exchanges, the Quran's intent is to bring people back logically and thoughtfully, without belittling those addressed. Again, the ultimate priority must be understood to be the preservation of virtue, and the Quran does not take sides outside of this all-important measure.

The third point I'll raise in addressing misconceptions about the Quran relates to the other major monotheistic religions. As was stated in an earlier section, Stories of the Quran, a good part of the Quran discusses past religions and past prophets, with a substantial portion of that discussion directed toward affirming the foundations of the other two monotheistic faiths: Judaism and Christianity. Again, the Quran affirms the virgin birth of Jesus, the miracles performed by Jesus, the prophethood of Moses, the miracles performed by Moses, and the journey of the Exodus.

I have often wondered why the Quran—a book revealed to Muslims— spends so much time affirming the foundations of the other two monotheistic faiths. After all, Jews have their own set of scriptures, as do the Christians, so why the repetition within the Quran? This repetition, along with its associated "real estate," must also be put into perspective with regard to the relative size of the Quran to that of other texts. For instance, the Quran contains less than one-fifth the number of verses in the Bible, and unlike the plurality of other texts, the Quran represents the sole divine book within the Islamic faith. Of course, a partial answer to this question may be that the god views all monotheistic religions as having a set of commonalities, which in the end can bring these religions and their members closer to each other. While this may be a plausible viewpoint, it is not the real reason for the Quran's affirmation of the Jewish and Christian foundations, which I only recently came to appreciate.

Lately, I have begun to notice an increasing trend within popular Western culture to discredit and call into question certain miracles that have constituted the foundations of the Jewish and Christian faiths over the years. Even the historical existence of some prophetic characters was called into question. Thus, I have come to believe that the real reason the Quran reiterates and reaffirms these foundations is because the Quran wants to

---

21. I think of this main message as the Quran's assertion that it embodies truth and Haqq both in its totality and its details, but this message should not be construed as encouraging blind acceptance; in essence it does not, as we'll see demonstrated through many of the verses we will examine throughout this book.

challenge this questioning itself. In this respect, the Quran can be perceived as saying, "If you want to challenge these foundations, discredit my miraculous nature first, and if you cannot, then accept these foundations as truth." Ironically, it seems—if we are to subscribe to this rationale for this repetition—that the Quran may ultimately be destined to be "the keeper" of the Jewish and Christian faiths—yet another reason why the Quran should not be only viewed as the book of the Muslims. Of course, billions of people around the world today believe the Jewish and Christian foundations to be real and beyond any doubt. Nonetheless, these foundations are matters of pure faith, as no one today can prove they took place, which is perhaps the reason why some have begun to question their occurrence. The Quran's affirmation is therefore important; if we can entertain the miraculous nature of the Quran, such affirmation perhaps even elevates the status of these foundations from pure faith to independently verified fact. In this sense, the Quran becomes not only the timeless miracle it is claimed to be but also one that captures and authenticates the essence of every divine message ever bestowed on man by the god (remember, the Quran talks of the existence of numerous prophets and religions, the majority of which are unknown to those reading the Quran).

Let me conclude this section by proposing we consider adopting a new understanding of the Quran that's based on the Quran's reverence for virtue, regardless of where that virtue may be found. And in spite of the relative brevity of this discussion, I hope I built a convincing case against recent criticisms of the Quran as perhaps being somewhat shortsighted and, based on my comprehension of the Quran, not reflective of a proper understanding of either its depth or its totality (facts that are probably unknown to many Muslims today as well). I will even go further and prompt my readers to think open-mindedly of the Quran as a book that sincerely attempts to establish foundations for peace and coexistence, not conflict and hatred. It is also a book that never means to force its teachings or philosophy but instead sincerely strives to *help* humanity at the individual and collective levels, in the present and for the future.

Quran Sample Chapter

It's time to look at two excerpts of chapters from the Quran. The verses I present in this section constitute the beginning of the Quran itself and then the first twenty-seven verses of the chapter "The Rahman," which contains a total of seventy-eight verses. The chapter of the Rahman is considered by many to be one of the most beautiful and engaging chapters of the Quran.

My mother tells a story of the chapter of the Rahman from when she was a little girl living in Baghdad. My grandfather told her that once, when he was sitting in the famous and beautiful Kadhimeya mosque in Baghdad (the burial site of the prophet Muhammad's fourth and sixth great grandsons, themselves revered spiritual leaders), a man with an unusually attractive voice and recitation method started to recite the chapter of the Rahman. My grandfather reported that as soon as this man recited the first few verses, the mosque had completely filled with listeners, and within a couple of weeks, almost everyone in Baghdad was talking about it. The man who was reciting this chapter turned out to be none other than Abdul-Basit, the Egyptian reader I mentioned earlier, the person responsible for introducing me to the Quran. Abdul-Basit was apparently "on tour" when he stopped by several neighboring countries, and the people of Baghdad were fortunate enough to have hosted him that night. This was also back in the early 1950s, when tape recorders were not common household items, so the majority of locals did not possess the means to listen to such a recitation unless they were able to be there in person.

Rahman is one of the "names" of the god, as well as one of his core attributes. The word *Rahman* comes from a more primitive word that means "a mother's womb." And just like the womb protects and nourishes the growing fetus inside it, Rahman too protects and nourishes all of the god's creation. Rahman has also been commonly translated as the one with mercy, love, or compassion.

Another Arabic word that is closely related to Rahman is *Raheem*. Raheem means essentially the same thing as Rahman, but it takes on a slightly different expressive form. In addition, the combination of these two words as "the Rahman, the Raheem" takes on special significance within the Quran. First, the expression *in [or through] the name of the god the Rahman, the Raheem* is an expression that precedes every chapter in the Quran except one and is read prior to reading the first verse; some even consider it a distinct verse. Second, the Quran begins with verses that contain this expression.

The first chapter of the Quran is called "The Opening." The chapter of the Opening is seven verses long and must be recited with each of the five daily prayers. The Opening begins with the following three verses:

> *In the name of the god, the Rahman, the Raheem. Let all thanks belong [or return] to the god, the life giver and life sustainer of all worlds [or existences]. The Rahman, the Raheem.*

(1:1–3)

The chapter of the Rahman is special in many different ways. First, it stresses the important virtue of justice and urges its reverence and protection. Next, it mentions the humble beginnings from which we, as a species, came. It also directs attention to many natural wonders in an attempt to engage the reader's thinking and introspection. Additionally, it mentions "gifts" bestowed upon humanity by the god and continually asks, "So which of your life giver's gifts do you deny?" which further engages the reader's thoughtfulness. It's also a chapter that describes the place known as "paradise" in good detail and through rather pointed and highly expressive imagery. Finally, the chapter mentions creatures called *jann* (or *jinn*), also mentioned in other places in the Quran. These creatures seem to occupy a parallel reality or existence to our own but who are nonetheless almost completely isolated from us.

The chapter of the Rahman is a highly expressive and eloquent chapter, with a mostly single rhyme that rhymes with the English words *can* and *man*. When voiced by a capable reader, such as Abdul-Basit, it is difficult not to pay full attention to and seriously contemplate what is being read and said, as the verses below hopefully illustrate:

> The Rahman,
> Taught the Quran,
> Created man,
> Taught him how to understand [or differentiate between right
>   and wrong].
> The sun and the moon are under [or through, by] calculation,
> And the stars and trees are bowing [or prostrating],
> And the sky he [the god] erected and placed the scales [of
>   justice],
> So that you [humanity] do not exploit [or overcome] the scales,
> And that you measure fairly, and that you do not abolish [or
>   shortchange] the scales.
> And Earth [or the land] he [the god] laid for the living [or
>   people].
> On her are fruits and clustered palm trees,
> And encased grains and sweet-scented flowers.
> So which of your life giver's gifts do you [humanity and jinn]
>   deny?
> [The god] created man from clay like earthenware,[22]
> And created the jann [or jinn] from pure fire [or energy, not
>   matter].
> So which of your life giver's gifts do you deny?
> The life giver [or sustainer] of the two easts and the two wests.
> So which of your life giver's gifts do you deny?
> The two seas come together,

22. The creation of life and that of man is discussed in chapter 7.

Between them is a wall [or barrier] so as to not exceed each
   other [or completely mix together].
So which of your life giver's gifts do you deny?
From both come pearls and corals.
So which of your life giver's gifts do you deny?
And to him [the god] belong the established ships in the sea that
   *look [or appear] like mountains.*23
So which of your life giver's gifts do you deny?
Everyone on her [Earth] will vanish,
But the face of your [Muhammad's] life giver will remain
   forever glorious; forever remain filled with giving.

                                                    (55:1–27)

---

23. These ships are discussed in chapter 9.

2 The Last Prophet

If the Quran can be considered to be an extraordinarily beautiful book, it can likewise be said that Muhammad was an equally extraordinary character. We'll learn more about this character in this chapter, in which I attempt to summarize the important events that shaped Muhammad's life and provide a brief overview of his character, mission, and teachings. Muhammad was a man who, as many believe, was not only responsible for "delivering" the Quran to humanity but also took it upon himself to constantly learn from, grow with, and live his daily life through its messages, teachings, and philosophy.

Birth and Youth

Muhammad was born in the year 570 CE in the city of Mecca in present-day Saudi Arabia. He was an only child, and he lost his parents at a very early age. Muhammad's father, Abdullah, passed away when Muhammad was still in his mother's womb; his mother, Aminah, died when Muhammad was about six years old.

Following his mother's death, Muhammad was adopted by his grandfather, Abdul-Muttaleb, a revered elder gentleman within Arabia. Muhammad remained under his grandfather's care until Abdul-Muttaleb's death two years later, at which point Muhammad was adopted into his uncle's household, where he was apparently welcomed with considerable care and love. Later in life, Muhammad spoke of his adopted mother as "my second mother," while his adopted father (also Ali's father) helped and protected Muhammad throughout Muhammad's adult life but especially during the critical period that followed the initial revelation when Muhammad began preaching his message to the larger Meccan community.

Not much is known about Muhammad's early childhood and teen years, as the earliest reports of his character began to surface when he was about twenty years old, which was twenty years before he received his first revelation. During this early period of his life, Muhammad earned the nickname "the honest [or truthful] and trustworthy one" by fellow members of his community.

An Appropriate Nickname

In one particular incident during Muhammad's youth, a sudden flash flood engulfed the Ka'ba. The Ka'ba, located in Mecca, is the place of pilgrimage for present-day Muslims and is believed to have been erected by the prophet Abraham (the same prophet we met in chapter 1) with the help of his elder son, Ishmael, as a "house for God," where those seeking the god can freely meditate and worship. As such, the Ka'ba was considered a sacred destination and frequently visited by many near and far tribes living within the general area of the Arabian Peninsula at the time.

During this particular flash flood, the holy black stone that sits at the site (believed to be the same stone in the present-day Ka'ba) fell down and had to be reestablished. Because of its religious significance, representatives from various powerful tribes started to argue as to which tribe should have the honor of restoring this sacred part of the structure. Heated argument thus ensued but no amicable conclusion could be reached, so they all agreed to refer the matter to a fair and trustworthy arbiter to settle this seemingly insurmountable dispute.

They unanimously agreed that no one was more suited to handle the matter than Muhammad, the honest and trustworthy one, and so they called on him to help come up with an amicable solution. Muhammad asked that a large piece of cloth be made. He then placed the holy stone in the center of this cloth and asked each tribe to nominate a representative to grab a portion of the cloth edges. With Muhammad's help, the stone was restored, and the highly sensitive matter was resolved quickly and peacefully through the participation of all claimants. The word *peacefully* must be emphasized here, as sensitive disputes such as this could have easily turned into a decade-long war between various tribes, as history has repeatedly demonstrated for that society during such times.

Also during this time (and possibly due to his reputation for honesty and a strong work ethic), Muhammad worked as a trader representing the financial interests of wealthy individuals. During the hot Arabian summer months, Muhammad led trading caravans north, between Mecca and present-day Syria, while during the cooler winter months he led these caravans south, between Mecca and present-day Yemen. Before continuing with our story, though, it's worthwhile to pause at this point to examine the general Arabian society of the time and in the process become a bit more familiar with commonly practiced religious norms and beliefs that contributed to Muhammad's early mental and spiritual dispositions.

Arabian Society Before Muhammad

The Arabs of the sixth century generally consisted of various tribes that lived in and around towns and cities located within the general vicinity of the larger Arabian Peninsula. Muhammad's own tribe was one of the largest and most powerful tribes, called "Quraish" (Arabic for "sharklike"). Not all was good between these various tribes, however, as tribal wars, raids, rape, and pillaging, among other atrocities, were quite frequent events. As I stated earlier, it was not uncommon for a minor incident to turn into many cycles of violence and revenge; at times it could even turn into many years of full-blown war.

In terms of the religious practices of the time, most Arabs of the period worshipped a collection of idols (or statues) that were made from various stone and wooden materials. Arabs believed these idols to be intermediaries between humanity and God, whose existence the Arabs generally recognized. Among this majority, a religious minority known as "the monotheists" coexisted, who, unlike the rest of the Arabs, did not believe in the sanctity of these statues nor believed them to hold any special religious significance. To understand where these monotheists came from and how they developed such a distinct belief, one must go back three to four thousand years earlier in time, to the time of Abraham and his journey to Arabia with his elder son, Ishmael, as later reported by the Quran. As I stated earlier, the purpose of this journey was to construct and dedicate a special house for God in Mecca, a location specially chosen by Abraham himself due to its arid and desolate nature. According to the Quran, Abraham did not want his followers to be "tempted" by locating this house in a lush and plentiful area, an attitude clearly reflective of Abraham's negative experience with idol worshippers from "greener Iraq," as was described in chapter 1. However, by the time of Muhammad a few thousand years later, Mecca had apparently lost its envisioned sacredness, and instead of being an environment of complete devotion to the one god, it had turned into an "impure marketplace" for idols and idol worshipping. For instance, it was not uncommon for these "little gods" to be repeatedly bought and sold and at times even eaten (some were made from dates) in the Ka'ba. This generally unholy atmosphere clearly went against the essence of the original Abrahamic monotheist belief of total dedication to the one god, without any lesser or undeserving worldly mediation.

From a young age, Muhammad despised these idols, along with the impurities they brought forth, and saw them facilitating much trouble and suffering within his society. On one occasion while traveling to Syria on behalf of his employer, Muhammad apparently entered into a heated discussion with a particular merchant. Because he was naturally quiet and soft-spoken, this discussion attracted the attention of other members of Muhammad's party, who began to wonder why he was so upset. It turned out that the merchant was insisting that Muhammad swear by two of these idols and had accused him of being a liar because Muhammad would not do so. Muhammad reportedly told the merchant, "I will never swear by these stones!" and the Syrian recognized the matter as hopeless and eventually gave in. Also around this time, Muhammad reportedly had taken trips to a nearby hill in the vicinity of Mecca to meditate and pray. The city of Mecca was (and still is) surrounded by a number of rough and rocky hills, and it was during these trips that Muhammad found much solace and tranquility away from the hustle and bustle of the city. We'll revisit the significance of these visits later in this chapter, when I discuss the initial revelation of the Quran.

The Dream

One of the caravans that Muhammad represented as a trader was owned by a wealthy, beautiful, and noble woman named Khadija. She was twice widowed, fifteen years Muhammad's senior, and by all accounts a woman of very high virtue. Khadija gained her wealth through her father, Khuwaylid ibn Asad, a successful businessman, whose vast wealth and business talents were inherited by his daughter, who successfully managed her father's business interests and preserved the family's fortune.

Khadija had an elder cousin named Waraqa, whom Khadija trusted and regularly sought advice from. Waraqa was a monotheist, a seer, an interpreter of dreams, and an "older wise man." He was also a highly read individual who possessed considerable knowledge of many of the common monotheist scriptures of the time, and it was through Waraqa that Khadija had gained a strong interest in the monotheist faith. On one particular occasion, Khadija came to Waraqa with a dream in which she witnessed a bright light enter her house and later enter and exit her own body. Waraqa immediately realized the significance of the dream, as he firmly believed from his study of the monotheist scriptures that a final monotheistic prophet from the line of Abraham was near. This last prophet would end the succession of prophets that started with Adam and continued through Noah, Abraham, Moses, and Jesus (although the line diverged at Abraham, as was noted in chapter 1). Waraqa carefully listened to Khadija and followed up by asking a few questions. He then invited her to be glad and hopeful and informed her that the light she saw was representative of the light of this last prophet.

News of the Last Prophet

As stated earlier, Muhammad had become an employee within Khadija's trading business. Shortly thereafter, when Muhammad was about twenty-five years old, Khadija had begun to take more notice—albeit from a distance—of her new employee. It's not clear what prompted such keen interest in Muhammad, other than perhaps his special nature.

On one of Muhammad's trading trips, Khadija instructed one of her other employees to keep a close eye on Muhammad and asked the man to report back on "everything" that involved Muhammad. Historical reports indicate that two incidents took place during this trip, both of which helped cement Khadija's belief that Muhammad was the last prophet who Waraqa told her about not too long before. The first was the incident with the Syrian merchant mentioned earlier, where Muhammad refused to swear by the idols. The second incident, however, was of much greater significance.

On the way back to Mecca during a scorching hot day, Muhammad's caravan decided to stop and rest for a while. Muhammad left the caravan and secluded himself by an old tree in the distance. Shortly after sitting down at the base of this tree, a stranger came rushing toward Muhammad. The eager man turned out to be a monk who happened to live and worship at a nearby monastery.

The monk greeted Muhammad and began to ask a few rather pointed questions.[24] "What is your name?" the monk asked. "My name is Muhammad," the reply came back. "Where are you from?" "I am from Mecca." "To which tribe (or clan) does your family belong?" Again Muhammad responded. The monk went on, "My son, will you allow me to uncover your shirt and look at the back side of your shoulder?" Muhammad gave the monk permission to look. Of course, all this was happening under the watchful eye of Khadija's hired observer. The monk was now through with his questioning and began to tell Muhammad, "My son, it has been known within our monastery that no one should sit where you sat, on the day that you sat, except he who is the last prophet." He then reached out and kissed Muhammad on the forehead and said, "When I saw you sit down, I came rushing to ask you the questions I did and to notice the mark on your back shoulder. And my son, I bear witness that you are that last prophet."

This obviously must have been quite shocking to Muhammad. No one had ever mentioned anything about a "last prophet" to him, let alone that *he* was that last prophet! We must realize that this incident took place many years before Muhammad received his first revelation, when he was "officially notified" that he was indeed the last prophet.[25] In any event, Khadija

---

24. In another account, these questions are posed to Khadija's other employee, prior to the monk meeting Muhammad.

25. In addition to this account, historians report another story in which a monk named Bahira witnessed a cloud moving along with a traveling party, apparently shielding them from the hot sun. Bahira—who was also familiar with the prophecy

was briefed about these happenings and after consulting with Waraqa now firmly believed that Muhammad was destined to become the last prophet promised by the monotheistic scriptures of the time.

Marriage Proposal

At some point following this incident with the monk, Khadija apparently began to develop feelings toward Muhammad, even though she had turned down every marriage proposal that had come her way until then. One of Khadija's maids had apparently begun to take notice of these feelings, along with Khadija's facial expression when the name Muhammad was mentioned in her presence. When the maid attempted to inquire about this, however, Khadija would quickly dismiss the inquiry. Eventually, she started to slowly confide her feelings to this maid as the weeks and months passed by. The maid immediately offered to help and told her lady to "leave the matter to me."

The maid then went to see Muhammad. "Why aren't you married?" she asked. "Because I do not possess the means to marry," Muhammad replied. The maid then asked, "Supposing that this was not a problem and that the woman is beautiful, intelligent, and from a good family, would you agree to marry?" "But suppose that she did not want to marry me!" the reply came back. "That's my business, you don't worry about that; I just want to know that, if the qualities I mentioned are present, would you in principle agree to marriage?" Muhammad remained silent, and his silence was interpreted as agreement.

Based on numerous eyewitness accounts, Muhammad was probably about 6 feet (2 m) tall, possessed a medium to athletic (muscular) build, a broad chest, large eyes, white skin, and black wavy hair. By virtually all accounts he was quite a handsome man. All of this was complemented by Muhammad's sense of virtue and humble personality. Also, Muhammad

---

of a final Arabian prophet from the line of Abraham—asked the party to join him for dinner. However, upon closely examining everyone, he asked them if anyone was left behind. "Yes, a boy stayed behind to watch our goods," they responded. "Bring him, and let him not miss our gathering!" Bahira requested. When he saw Muhammad, who was then nine years old, Bahira immediately realized the boy's significance. He began asking him some pointed questions while also taking notice of the mark on Muhammad's back between his shoulder blades, all of which confirmed the identity of the last prophet as reported within the scriptures in Bahira's possession. When Bahira became almost certain that this boy was destined to be the last prophet, he asked Muhammad's uncle, "Who is Muhammad's father?" "I am his father," responded the uncle (it was somewhat shameful for someone to be an orphan in Arabia at the time). "You cannot be the father," Bahira countered, "for we've learned that the last prophet must be one who is an orphan."

was, and remained, a simple family man who seldom took pleasure in the pleasurable things of his day. When asked about this later in life, he replied, "Prayer is my pleasure, and prayer is where I am my happiest."

The combination of all of this arguably led Khadija to become attracted to Muhammad and her subsequent marriage proposal to him. When Muhammad was twenty-five years old, Muhammad and Khadija were married, and this marriage lasted until Khadija's death some twenty-five years later. During this time, Khadija was Muhammad's only wife, and the marriage was, by virtually all accounts, a completely blissful one. Muhammad and Khadija were blessed with six children, although not all survived into adolescence.[26]

Encounter with the Heavens

I stated earlier that Muhammad would, from time to time, seek solitude and meditate at a nearby hill outside Mecca. He continued this practice after his marriage to Khadija and found her extremely supportive in preparing his food and water and at times even traveling to the hill herself to meditate and pray with him. During one of these trips, while Muhammad was in his late thirties, he heard a voice that said, "Muhammad, I am Jubraeel" (the biblical archangel Gabriel). Upon hearing the strange and unexpected voice, Muhammad rushed down the mountain engulfed with fear and anxiety and immediately told his wife what had just happened. Khadija comforted him and told him not to worry. This incident occurred a second time several

---

26. Contrary to common belief, some scholars have suggested that Khadija was only a few years older than Muhammad, that she did not marry prior to Muhammad, and that three of the daughters believed to be Muhammad's were actually daughters of her deceased sister who had also lost their father. The daughters then came into Khadija's household and were adopted by Khadija and Muhammad. According to this account, the only surviving child from Muhammad's marriage to Khadija (and from Muhammad's later marriages) was Fatima. Fatima, acknowledged as the youngest daughter, holds special significance for other reasons. The prophet was once asked who his most beloved person was, to which he replied, "Fatima." Fatima had in turn so loved and cared for her father that she was frequently referred to as "her father's mother" by her contemporaries. Fatima was also Ali's wife and the mother of Hassan and Hussain, considered within the Shia or Shi'ite branch of Islam to be the second and third of twelve spiritual guides (Ali being the first). Hassan and Hussain were also the only men through whom the line of Muhammad in the form of direct descendants, also known in Iraq as *Sayyed* (male, singular) and *Alaweyya* (female, singular), continues through our present day. My mother once told me that my great-grandmother, whom I had the privilege of meeting in 1975, was such a direct descendant (direct descendants are traced only through the male line).

months later, and Khadija again told Muhammad not to be anxious. On the third occurrence, however, something profound took place.

Muhammad was now exactly forty years of age. While on the hill (actually a cave in the hill), a man appeared to Muhammad. The man faced Muhammad, held him firmly by the shoulders, and while forcefully shaking him cried (or shouted), "Read!" Muhammad replied, "I do not read!" (Muhammad was illiterate and remained so throughout his life). The man shook Muhammad a second time and again uttered the word, "Read!" Again, Muhammad proclaimed in fear, "I do not read!" On the third exchange, however, the man uttered the first verses of the Quran to be revealed:

> *Read! Through the name of your life giver, the one who created. Created man from alaq.*[27] *Read! Through your life giver's extreme generosity. The one who taught [or gave knowledge] through the pen. Taught man that which he did not know.*
>
> (96:1–5)

The man turned out to be the angel Gabriel in human form, and the first two encounters were to ease the shock of the third. The prophethood of the last prophet thus began and would last for the next twenty-three years—the period of time through which the Quran was fully revealed.[28]

Following this third encounter, Muhammad again rushed down to Khadija, but he was now noticeably shivering and shaking and asked her to cover him with blankets. Upon hearing what Muhammad had just experienced, she replied in her usual comforting manner, "Do not fear, for God will never disgrace you. For you have always loved your family, and you help and are kind to anyone who is sick or in need. You are generous to your visitors. You have endured many hardships on the path of truth, and you have devoted yourself to all that is good."

As soon as Muhammad was calm again, Khadija went to visit her cousin and trusted mentor Waraqa. Waraqa asked that she return with Muhammad so that he could hear firsthand all that had transpired in the cave. The three gathered, and Waraqa began to listen to what Muhammad had experienced. After Muhammad finished, Waraqa uttered these historic words: "I wish I had been young this day and that I could live to see the

---

27. A discussion of *alaq* (or *alaqa*) is provided in chapter 8.

28. It's not known with certainty which verse(s) were the last one(s) to be revealed. However, it's well accepted that Muslims were made aware of the prophet's soon-to-come passing shortly before the prophet's death. (Some have claimed that verses 110:1–3 were the last verses, since they clearly allude to the end of the prophet's mission.)

day that your people will drive you out, so that I can help you on that day." "Are my people going to drive me out?" Muhammad asked. "Yes," Waraqa replied. "They will drive you out. For there is not a single prophet who has come with the truth that you bear and not been driven out of his homeland."

The New Message

During the first three years following the initial revelation, Muhammad slowly and secretly preached the new faith and started to win over converts, who were mostly composed of the poor and disadvantaged men and women of Mecca. And even though he was a trusted and respected member of a powerful clan and this clan was in turn a member of the most powerful tribe in Arabia, Muhammad, along with his new message, was initially met with substantial resistance.

Muhammad's message focused on preaching the importance of going back to the one god and the inherent equality between master and slave, black and white, rich and poor. However, such notions of equality and abandoning idols for one god did not sit well with the then-powerful and wealthy classes of Arabia. At one point during this period, a number of tribal leaders, along with a few wealthy individuals, gathered and decided to put an end to this new "nonsense." They initially pursued a diplomatic approach and invited Muhammad's uncle (the same uncle who adopted Muhammad after the death of his grandfather), a well-respected and powerful individual himself, to talk some sense into Muhammad and request that he immediately abandon his teachings.

As they gathered, they asked the uncle, "What is it your nephew wants? If he wants to be our master, we will appoint him our chief. If he wants wealth, we will shower him with wealth. If he wants women, we will divorce our most beautiful wives and gift them to Muhammad." The uncle returned to Muhammad and informed him of this new proposal by Mecca's most revered and powerful individuals. On hearing it, however, Muhammad immediately replied with these now famous words: "Uncle, tell them that even if they could bring down the sun and place her in my right hand and if they could bring down the moon and place her in my left hand so that I abandon that which I have been asked to do, I will not do such a thing!"

With their offer plainly rejected, the tribal leaders then decided to pursue other, violent means in an attempt to squash the new faith. The ten-year period that followed was a time of immense suffering for anyone who was either a member or supporter of this new faith. The early Muslims were subjected to various forms of boycott, torture, divorce (two of Muhammad's own daughters were so divorced), and even murder, the purpose of which was to terrorize and intimidate anyone associated with Muhammad and his new religion. At one point toward the end of this period, Muhammad and his followers were driven to a location at the outskirts of Mecca in what amounted to living in nothing less than a World War II concentration camp. Residents were denied basic human needs and were forced to live (and die) under extremely difficult circumstances. This was a period of tremendous hardship for Muhammad.

Sad Times

Although naturally an outgoing and pleasant individual, Muhammad was seen crying on many occasions as he witnessed the suffering of those who believed and trusted in him. Muhammad, nonetheless, continued to preach patience and told his followers that their suffering would one day come to an end. Also during this period, his wife, friend, confidant, comforter, adviser, and the mother of his children, Khadija, died—quite possibly due to the severe conditions this once wealthy and powerful woman was forced to live in.

Combined with everything else that was taking place, Khadija's death threw Muhammad into a state of utter shock and sadness. Muhammad would in later years recount, "The god has not given me anyone as good as Khadija. When people denied me, she believed. She affirmed me when people called me a liar. When people deprived me, she supported me, and the god gave me children through her." Up until the moment of his death, Muhammad always remembered Khadija with moving love and sadness. And although left as the sole caretaker of Muhammad and Khadija's four daughters, Muhammad did not take a second wife for a number of years following Khadija's death. I think that if anyone should ever doubt the famous adage "Behind every great man is a woman," they need not look any further than Muhammad's own example.

At the end of this tumultuous period, Muhammad, along with his remaining followers, migrated (remember Waraqa's prophetic words) to the city of Medina where, unlike in his native Mecca, he was warmly welcomed. In Medina, Muhammad solidified the foundations of the new faith and way of life, and it was in this new homeland that the young Muslim community began to emerge. This migration was of great significance, marking the start of a new era as well as the beginning of the present-day Islamic calendar. Muhammad remained in Medina for the next ten years, until his death at the age of sixty-three, twenty-three years after the initial revelation had taken place. However, two years prior to his death, Muhammad marched to Mecca following the Meccans' violation of an important peace treaty struck between them and the Muslims. Muhammad "liberated" Mecca without any loss of life and did not force any of its residents to unwillingly accept the new faith, in spite of the hardship and suffering the Meccans had inflicted on him and his followers.

Examining a Claim

As I stated in chapter 1, Muhammad claimed that he was the last prophet sent by the god to humanity, and this claim is also stated in the Quran. I would like to now explore the strength of this claim, since it goes to the heart of the credibility of the Quran and because we now have more than fourteen hundred years of "observational evidence" to carefully scrutinize. Before doing so, though, I'll need to explain what the word *prophet* means, or at least how it's understood and used by the Quran.

A prophet is generally understood to be someone chosen by the god to reveal or communicate something important to humanity. There are two terms that signify the role of such a person within the Quran: prophet and messenger. A messenger generally holds a much greater mission than that of a prophet, and historically there have been many more prophets than messengers. In addition, some of these select individuals hold titles to being both prophets and messengers. Moses, Jesus, and Mohammad, for example, are all considered by the Quran to be both prophets and messengers, since their respective missions were of great importance to humanity. In this book, however, I use only the term *prophet* and not *messenger* for Muhammad, to avoid unnecessary confusion, with the understanding that he was both a prophet and a messenger. So what exactly is the Quran's definition for a prophet?

As noted, a prophet is someone who is first and foremost *chosen* by the god. As such, this person must claim that he "comes on behalf of" the god.[29] Next, the prophet's claim must be accompanied by "proof" to substantiate his coming on behalf of the god. This proof has traditionally been in the form of certain miracles or extraordinary things that simply cannot be duplicated outside of the influence and power of the god. And last, this person must bring forth some revelation, message, or communication to either his immediate people or to the larger family of humanity (meaning that the message is valid for all). These are the essential qualifications to becoming a prophet in the eyes of the Quran. It is simply not enough for someone to live a life of virtue and thus be elevated within his or her religion to a special rank or status for that person to be considered a prophet or equivalent to a prophet. There are many examples of such "promotion" that have taken place since man began to walk Earth, and they will probably continue to take place well into the future. Let's now assess the Quran's claim that Muhammad was the last such prophet.

This claim was made more than fourteen hundred years ago. Thus far—keeping in mind the qualifications to be a prophet—the claim appears to

---

29. Prophets and messengers have traditionally only been male.

hold true.[30] The world, it can be argued, has not seen a person exhibiting such qualifications since the death of Muhammad.[31] It's also important that we consider the length of this time span. For example, the time frame between the appearances of Jesus and Muhammad was about six hundred years. It's also believed that the time frame between Moses and Jesus was about thirteen hundred years, within which many other prophets were reported to have emerged. These include the prophets Aaron (Moses's brother), King David, King Solomon, and Elijah, among scores or perhaps even hundreds of others, as reported by both Jewish and Christian scriptures as well as by the Quran.

It's also important to consider the tremendous growth in the human population, along with the stunning degree of cultural and technological change. Even though no one knows with any certainty what the global population was fourteen hundred years ago, a rough estimate of around 200 million is probably close. It's almost 7 billion today, representing an almost 3500 percent increase. I think it would be somewhat strange for a god to leave humanity "prophetless" during such a population explosion, unless this god had a definite plan for when a final communication with humanity should occur. (The million dollar question is why should there even be a final communication?) In other words, given this large population explosion, you might expect to see a proportional increase in the number of prophets, but this has arguably not occurred, at least not yet. The length of this fourteen-hundred-year time frame therefore becomes somewhat significant in its absence of any new monotheistic prophet, and the Quran's claim that Muhammad was the last prophet appears to remain, thus far, true. One can certainly disagree with the assertion that Muhammad was a prophet, making this argument somewhat pointless. A reasonable response for that may be that there is more evidence available in support of Muhammad being a prophet than there is evidence to suggest that he was not. An important component of this evidence—but not the only or even most important evidence—is what I intend to present during the remainder of this book. I started out this chapter by alluding to

---

30. Although the term "prophet" has been ascribed to individuals after Muhammad, it's important to remember the Quran's definition for prophet when evaluating this assertion.

31. In my view, it is not only important that a person claiming to be a prophet provide evidence for such a claim but that such evidence is strong enough to refute the Quran and counter its claim that Muhammad was the final prophet (meaning that the evidence provided by a prophet must be stronger than the "miracle of the Quran"). This also means that such evidence is "living" and accessible so that it can be readily examined at any time by others (since the Quran too is readily accessible and can be examined at any time).

Muhammad's extraordinary character. Let's next touch on certain aspects of his character, along with a short discussion of his mission and teachings.

Character and Teachings

Muhammad's teachings centered on building one's character by attaining higher levels of virtue through the practice of various acts of such virtue, such as kindness, compassion, and forgiveness. Muhammad preached the importance of trust; helping others; and serving one's family, neighbors, and community. He stressed the importance of attaining higher levels of knowledge and the responsibility of respecting one's elders while being kind and generous to one's juniors. He taught the virtues of maintaining good health, cleanliness, and general hygiene. Muhammad taught the importance of moderation and maintaining a sense of balance in all life affairs and of "taking the middle road." One of the areas of moderation stressed by Muhammad was moderation during religious acts and commitments, and on numerous occasions he asked his followers to avoid religious zealotry and intolerance. In my judgment, however, and perhaps in the view of many Islamic and Western scholars, Muhammad's teachings regarding the status and treatment of women within one's family and extended society are some of the most significant lessons he offered.

Within Arabian society prior to Muhammad, the very act of bringing a female into this world was seen as a lowly and shameful deed. Women were not only forbidden from possessing property or inheriting from their husbands, but they were also considered "property" in many respects. In terms of marriage and divorce, men were allowed to marry a virtually unlimited number of wives, and women were not allowed to divorce their husbands. Men, on the other hand, could divorce their wives with a single passing declaration of divorce.

All this drastically changed with the advent of Muhammad. He taught that women should not only possess property but that such property be kept as personal assets that reverted to the wife in the event of a divorce. He also taught that women should be able to inherit from their husbands. In addition, men were no longer able to take an unlimited number of wives; instead, they had to stop at four, and only if a man could be physically, emotionally, and financially fair with all of his wives (even though the preference was, and is, for a man to take no more than one wife). Men now had to wait a period of time before a divorce could take effect, and women were able to divorce their husbands if they were able to show proper cause. Beyond this, Muhammad passionately and repeatedly strived to inspire men to respect, love, and revere women, as evidenced by so many prophetic sayings, a few of which we'll see in the next section. Muhammad's teachings and his general welcoming attitude toward women were also

complemented by the Quran, which I cannot read without understanding
· that men and women—although seen as holding different responsibili-
ties—are, in the most important respects, indeed equal in the eyes of the
· god. Given Muhammad's intolerant, ignorant, and male-dominated tribal
environment, I have often wondered whether any other individual in history has so eagerly and genuinely attempted to effect the same degree of
lasting positive change in the status and *cause* of women as Muhammad
attempted to within his own society almost a millennium and a half ago.

In terms of general demeanor, Muhammad was a quiet and soft-spoken
individual who seemed to be in an almost constant state of grace and seren-
ity. He maintained an easy and compassionate attitude and always greeted
his followers with a smile and a two-handed handshake. He was a sensitive
man who constantly sympathized with his followers and their suffering.
He was never reported to have transgressed, verbally or physically, upon
anyone, and treated all, including those who fought and harmed him, with
ample fairness and consideration. During times of battle against those
intending to crush the new faith, Muhammad taught the Muslims to not
harm the young, the elderly, women, or even trees. He treated captured
soldiers with kindness (quite contrary to how the Arab idolaters treated
captured Muslim soldiers), and many of them were released if a captured
soldier agreed to teach two Muslims how to read and write.

Muhammad apparently possessed such a gracious and forgiving nature
that the Quran itself intervened on his behalf in some of his affairs with
the Muslims. For example, the Quran told a group of individuals who had
visited the prophet too often and had apparently taken time the prophet
wanted to spend with his own family, "Do not overstay when you visit the
messenger of the god, for he does not find it within his heart to ask you to
leave, but the god is not ashamed of Haqq."[32] Reflecting on the prophet's
generally calm and compassionate demeanor in contrast with that of his
environment, my mother used to humorously exclaim, "Why did the god
send such a gentle and kind person to such a rough and difficult people
(the Arabs)?" And perhaps the most significant praise of Muhammad's
general character comes from the Quran itself:

> And you [Muhammad] surely possess the highest order of
> character [or virtue, behavior].
>
> (68:4)

It's perhaps no wonder then that the name "Muhammad," which in
Arabic means "praise-worthy" or "of high regard," was chosen for this

---

special man by his then-pregnant mother after she had a dream where she was asked to choose this name for her future son—a name unknown anywhere prior to that and which has become one of the most common in the world.[33] Muhammad firmly believed that his religion was a continua- tion of the religions of Moses and Jesus, and at times he would refer to his predecessors as "brothers." On one occasion, Muhammad and a group of followers passed by a house that was apparently under construction and thus missing a few bricks. He stopped and asked, "Do you see that house missing a few blocks?" "Yes, messenger of the god, we do," they replied. Muhammad continued, "My example to that of my brothers Moses and Jesus is that I am the missing block to their house. I was sent to complete that house."

Prophetic Sayings

It is not possible to provide a meaningful overview of the life of Muhammad without touching on the so-called prophetic sayings. The prophetic sayings are considered to be a major component of the Islamic faith and comprise what the prophet Muhammad was known (or believed) to have said during his lifetime, especially after becoming a prophet. Because the prophet—any prophet—is guided through the divine, as the belief goes, these sayings understandably take on an important teaching and religious dimension. In my own experience, I have always found that hearing first-hand what someone says provides the richest understanding of that person's character. And so I have included a special section in this chapter to provide a sample collection of Muhammad's sayings. The dilemma, however, was in deciding what to include, as there are thousands of these sayings, and providing even 5 percent of them is simply not practical.

In addition, I wanted the collection to accurately represent not only Muhammad's character and teachings but also his essence. This essence is perhaps well understood by those who have taken much interest in Muhammad's life and mission, as well as by those who have gained considerable exposure to and achieved a proper understanding of his sayings. I do not claim to be such a person myself, but I tried, nonetheless, to capture this essence as best as I understood it within the amount of space the book allowed. I also grouped these sayings according to their respective subject areas so we can better appreciate the breadth of the topics they cover.

---

33. *The Columbia Encyclopedia*, 6th ed., s.v. "Muhammad." The story of the foretelling that "Muhammad" will one day become one of the most common names in the world was reported to have been communicated to Muhammad by the angel Gabriel shortly after the new prophet was attacked and struck by several large stones during a visit to a nearby village.

Translating these sayings from the original Arabic may have led to certain inaccuracies that are perhaps unavoidable when translating between any two languages. My primary focus during translation, however, was to preserve what I believed to be the original and intended meaning, which is sometimes best communicated by avoiding a literal word-for-word translation. There are numerous other books available that may better communicate the original Arabic sayings, should anyone find gross inaccuracies present here.[34] So without further ado, let's now explore these sayings that reveal the essence of the last prophet. I recommend you take your time reading this section to better appreciate the meaning and the wisdom expressed here. ✳

On the god

- The god loves that when you do something, you do it with excellence.
- The god loves it when you are fair with all your children, even in kissing.
- The god loves a lie if it brings two [or close] people back together and hates a truth if it moves two [or close] people apart.
- The god does not look at your faces or your bodies but looks at your hearts and your doings.
- The god's accounting is simple and generous: If you intend to perform a virtue but do not do it, you will be granted one virtue [or credit]. If you do it, you will be granted ten virtues or much more. And if you intend to do something harmful but do not do it, you will be granted one virtue [or credit]. And if you do it, you will only be accounted for one sin [or debit].
- Beware of hurting [as in oppressing] anyone, for the god will surely avenge that person, even if the person was an atheist. And should one mountain needlessly hurt another, the god will surely smash the offending mountain.
- The god can forgive all a person's sins for simply clearing the path from something hurtful.
- The god says, "If someone seeks me out a little [or in small measures], I will seek them out a lot [or in large measures]. And if they walk toward me, I will run toward them."
- Think about everything, but not about what the god is.
- I once asked Gabriel, "Gabriel, have you ever seen the god?" And Gabriel answered, "Muhammad, between me and the god are one hundred layers [or walls, barriers] of light. If I even only look at the most distant layer [from the god], I will be completely consumed."
- The god will hold you accountable for all [the harm] that you do. Even

---

34. See the bibliography.

✳ These sayings are not part of the Koran.
  "   "   "   mostly " a code of (advice on) conduct.

if you needlessly harm a small bird, the god will bring that bird forth [on the Day of Judgment], and the bird will ask her god, "My life giver, ask this person, why did he needlessly harm me?"

■ Generosity is the god's most profound virtue [or attribute].

■ Know the god during your good and easy times, and he will know you during your hard and difficult ones. And know that the god loves to be asked.

■ If a discharge of semen is placed unto a stone, and the god had willed for that stone to turn into a child, the stone will surely turn into a child.

■ Purify your endeavors, for the god only accepts that which is pure.

On Knowledge

■ The god is sought through knowledge and is revered through knowledge. And the best things in this life and the next come with [or through] knowledge, and the worst things in this life and the next come with [or through] ignorance.

■ The most valuable people are the most knowledgeable.

■ The god will forgive forty sins from a knowledgeable man before he forgives a single sin from an ignorant one.

■ Teaching others good knowledge is better in the eyes of the god than *jihad* [Arabic for holy struggle in the way of the god].

■ Suleiman [the biblical King Solomon] was given the choice of being granted great wealth, becoming king, or acquiring knowledge. He chose knowledge, so the god gave him great wealth and made him king because he chose so wisely.

■ Seeking good knowledge is better in the eyes of the god than prayer, fasting, pilgrimage, and jihad in the way of the god.

■ Seeking an hour's knowledge is better [or rewards more] than praying the entire night. And one day's knowledge is better [or rewards more] than fasting for three months.

■ A knowledgeable man's sleep is better than an ordinary man's worship. And one prayer from a knowledgeable man equals thirty-five from an ignorant one.

■ Small actions when accompanied with knowledge are useful, and large actions when accompanied with ignorance are useless.

■ Acquire knowledge and learn, for the god does not pardon [intentional] ignorance. And write down what you know.

■ Seek knowledge from the cradle to the grave. Seek it even from China [as in far away].

■ Every great structure has a pillar that supports it, and the pillar that supports my religion is thoughtfulness.

- Should I live a day in which I do not learn something new that brings me closer to the god, then let that day's sunrise not shine on my face.

On Paradise

- Paradise is laid under the feet of mothers.
- There is a special place in paradise called the house of the generous, and only the most generous [in helping those in need] among you will see that place.
- In paradise, there is what no eye has seen, what no ear has heard, and what no heart has ever imagined.
- There are one hundred levels in paradise. Between each level and the next is like what is between our Earth and our heavens. And if the entirety of all of creation is placed into any one level, they [it] will all fit, with room to spare.
- Every lock has a key that unlocks it. And the key to paradise is in loving the poor and needy [or helpless].
- Every place has a path that leads to it, and the path that leads to paradise is knowledge.
- Moving from the difficulty of this life into the expansiveness of the next is like moving from the bounds and darkness of the womb into the expansiveness and light of this life.
- This life [its little significance] to the next is like comparing the [tiny] amount of water that sticks to a needle after the needle is placed in and taken out of the ocean with the whole ocean.

On Kindness

- If you meet an orphan, gently sweep his [or her] hair with your hand in kindness. For the god will grant you a virtue [or credit] for every single hair follicle your hand comes across.
- The god's mercy will meet you when you visit your sick friend. And when you meet him, gently hold his hand or comfort his face and ask, "How well are you feeling?"
- If you are about to overtake an enemy, let forgiveness be the price you pay for being stronger than he is.
- The best [man] among you is he who is best to his wife and daughters. No one [or man] is kind to women except he who is kindhearted, and no one [or man] is mean to women except he who is mean-hearted.
- I and the kind caretaker of an orphan are like this in paradise [here the prophet joined his index and middle fingers].
- Be kind. For kindness has never entered anything except that it made that thing more beautiful. And kindness has never left anything except

that it made that thing more repugnant. And the best form of kindness is that done toward your family and kin.

- If you should lead the public prayer, then ensure that you do not lengthen it. For among those praying are the young and old, and the weak and sick, and those needing to relieve themselves. But if you pray in private, then pray for as long as you want.
- The god will surely have mercy upon those who have mercy upon others.
- The god has demanded that you males take good care of your females. For they are your mothers, daughters, aunts, and sisters.

On Moderation

- Do not wrestle with religion, for you will always be beaten.
- How beautiful it is to worship the god but to do so moderately.
- Worship the god only to the extent of your capability, for the god does not tire until you tire.[35] And know that the most beloved acts of worship to the god are the ones that are done frequently, even if they are insignificant.
- Do not indulge yourself too deeply into matters of religion, for the god intended for it to be an easy matter, not a difficult one.
- Take pleasure in things, and be playful. For it pains me to see your religion [Islam] become a hard and cruel one.
- Do not practice religious extremism, for it will ruin you just as it ruined many before you.

On Helping

- He has not accepted my mission who sleeps with a full stomach while his neighbor sleeps with an empty one and he knew that his neighbor slept with an empty stomach.
- If the god wants something good to befall someone, he will allow that person to work in the service of other people.
- It is not jihad to grab your sword and start fighting. But jihad is to help support your parents and help support your children and support yourself so that you are not a burden to anyone.
- I entered paradise,[36] and I saw that charity rewards ten to one, while a loan rewards eighteen to one. And so I turned to Gabriel and asked, surprised, "Gabriel, how can it be that charity rewards less than a loan?" And Gabriel replied, "Because charity goes to those deserving and undeserving, but a loan only goes to those deserving."[37]

---

35. This is a figure of speech, since the Quran states that the god does not tire.
36. This is a reference to the prophet's "trip of the Ascension."
37. I find this saying rather interesting since the health of so much of our current

- Befriend the poor in this life, for they will have a strong say on the Day of Judgment.
- If you want your prayers to be answered, then help alleviate someone's difficulty.
- My helping someone in need is better to me than fasting an entire month or sitting and praying at the Ka'ba.

On Charity

- If you plant a tree, know that no bird, nor animal, nor human, shall eat from that tree, except that a virtue will be granted to you in the name of that which you have provided from that tree.
- Prevent grief and mishaps through acts of charity. And know that an act of charity can stop a mishap, even if that mishap has been predestined to immediately strike you.
- Serving your wife is a form of charity, and keeping a smile on your face is a form of charity, and giving good advice to someone who needs it is a form of charity, and providing directions to a lost person is a form of charity, and removing something harmful from the road is a form of charity.
- The best dinar [an old form of currency still in use today] in your pocket is the one you intend to spend on your family.
- Know that charity never lessens a person's wealth.
- The best form of charity is charity of the tongue [as in saying pleasant things].

On Health and Hygiene

- Maintaining clean dishes and a clean house brings you good fortune.
- The god loves those who are clean.
- Travel! For it brings you good health and more wealth. And return through a different path [from the one used to arrive at your destination].
- A prayer performed after you brushed your teeth [the Arabs used a special plant to brush their teeth] rewards seventy times more than a prayer without brushing your teeth.
- Eat less, and you will have a healthy body and a healthy mind.
- Help your sicknesses by drinking from cow's milk. For I hope that the god has given it many medicinal powers, since the cow eats from many different plants.

---

global economy is dependent upon the ability and willingness for people and institutions to lend to others.

- The god has not created a sickness except that he also created its cure, so seek all kinds of cure.
- Wish good health to others, and you too will be given good health.

On Faith

- Know that faith grows old in a person's heart, so ask the god to constantly refresh your faith.
- Jesus, son of Mary, once saw a man steal and so asked him, "Did you steal?" And the man replied, "No, by the one and only god, I did not steal." And Jesus said, "I believed in the god and believe that my eyes have lied."
- Faith is two halves; half is kind [or peaceful] patience, and the other is being thankful.
- Accept truths from all, young or old, even if they come from a foreign stranger or someone you hate. And reject untruths from all, young or old, even if they come from a beloved friend.
- The true believer is a servant of the god who does not hurt whom he hates and does not allow his friendships to stand in the way of truth. He keeps that which he is entrusted with and does not envy, gossip [for malice], or curse. He always tells the truth and does not call others with bad names. In prayer, he is thoughtful. In charity, he is quick. In hardship, he is patient and accepting. In ease, he is thankful. He does not want that which does not belong to him, and he is not stingy. He socializes to learn and discusses to understand. And if he is oppressed, he is patient until the Rahman gives him victory.

On Parents

- If you wish to live a long life, then be kind to your parents.
- Look into the faces of your elderly parents with a gaze of kindness and mercy. For if you do that, the god will grant you a virtue equal to that of performing a full and accepted pilgrimage—all for that one simple look.
- Love your mother, then love your mother, then love your mother, then love your father, then love the next closest [family member], and then the next [and so on].
- A parent's prayer for the child is surely heard by the god—and answered.
- No sin is punished faster than the sin of causing difficulty [or hardship] for your parents or the sin of needlessly hurting others.

On Marriage

- A woman is married for her spirituality or her wealth or her beauty. But try your best to win the woman with the most spirituality.

- If you want to propose to a woman and you have a few white hairs on your head, then make sure you tell her that you have a few white hairs on your head.
- When a man looks at his wife with kindness and his wife returns the same look, then the god too will look at them with the look of kindness and mercy.

On Being Thankful

- Know that when you say thank you to the god for a gift or blessing he has given you, these two words are better [or bigger] than that which you have been given, even if what you have received is a truly great and grand thing.
- Be thankful for the god's gifts to you, for they seldom return once they're gone.
- Those who do not thank people cannot be thankful to the god.

On Hope

- Know that victory comes with patience, relief comes with difficulty, and ease comes with hardship.
- Never despair! For if a hardship is so strong that it can burrow itself in the ground, its ease will be made so much stronger that it drives that hardship from its burrow.
- The god laughs at man's despair.[38]
- If these four things are available in you, then do not feel saddened by anything you may have missed in your life: truth in telling, trustworthiness, kindness, and eating from that which you worked hard to obtain.

On Wealth

- When a person dies, people say, "What did he leave behind [for us]?" And the angels say, "What did he leave behind for himself [in preparation for the next life]?"
- Wealth is in not needing anything from anyone. And if you must walk to someone for something, then walk slowly.
- Possessing beautiful hair is wealth, and possessing a beautiful face is wealth, and possessing a beautiful tongue is wealth, and money is wealth.
- Borrow less and you will live a freer life. And do not die owing a debt. And know that I do not buy something I cannot myself pay for.
- If you sell your home, then make sure that you at least buy a similar home or a better one.

---

38. The god "laughing" is also figure of speech.

On Friendships

- If you come back from a trip or want to visit someone, then take a gift with you. Take it even if the one you are visiting is a close neighbor, and even if your gift is but a pretty stone.
- If you are a group of three, then two should not whisper to each other without the third until you mix with more people, for that saddens the third.
- The god loves old friendships, so keep your friendships.
- Help your brother [in faith], whether he is oppressing or being oppressed. If he is being oppressed, help him. If he is oppressing, then stop him from it.
- The example of a good companion is like a perfume seller's store. Even if you miss being perfumed, you still smell the good odor of the store. And the example of a bad companion is like a blacksmith's store. Even if you miss being burned by flying sparks, you will be discomforted by the store's unsavory odor.

On Fairness

- If you hire someone, make sure you tell that person what you will pay him. And make sure you pay him before the sweat dries from his forehead.
- One hour's justice is better than one year's worship.
- If you build a wall between your house and your neighbor's, make sure that the wall is not so high that it stops the gentle breeze from reaching him.
- Beware of hurting someone who finds no help [or defense] from anyone except that from the god.
- Be humble toward he who helps you, even if it comes from a slave. And take that which rightfully belongs to you, even if you have to take from a wealthy Arab master.
- A just ruler is the god's shadow on this Earth. And should you enter a place [or area] that is absent a just ruler, do not stay.

On Social Conduct

- Practice consultation, for it protects against regret and wards off blame.
- Should you assemble together, then each person should wait for a turn to speak, and do not speak on top of each other. For if you do, then do not expect your assembly to be a good or useful one.
- Advise others to do well, even if you yourself cannot do much good. And advise others against something wrong, even if you yourself cannot avoid doing that wrong.

On Muhammad

- The god did not send me to be difficult or demanding but sent me to be mentoring and easygoing.
- I asked the god that he allow me to live as a meek and poor man and allow me to die as a meek and poor man. And when my time for resurrection comes, that I be resurrected with all those who are meek and poor.
- No one [or no prophet] has been hurt in the way of the god as much as I have been hurt in the way of the god.
- When I was young, I disliked idols and I disliked poetry. And I never wanted to do that which the other males did except twice, but the god protected [or prevented] me both times, and I never returned.
- Gabriel once told me, "Muhammad, live as long as you want, for you will surely die. And love whom you like, for you will surely leave them. And do whatever you like, for you will surely be held [accountable] to all that you do [good for good, and bad for bad]."
- I am so worried that your [Muslims'] affairs will be governed by the cruel and corrupt after my death.

On Interesting Observations

- Some sins cannot be forgiven through prayer, fasting, or pilgrimage. Such sins can only be forgiven through the difficulty encountered by a person's hard work in earning their sustenance.
- People have their own essences, just as the essence of gold is different from that of silver. And if someone tells you that a mountain has disappeared, believe it. But if someone tells you that someone's essence has changed, then do not believe it.
- The testimony of the one [who comes] from a village should not be taken above that of the one [who comes] from a city.
- There is nothing better than a thousand of its own kind, except man.
- Man is a strange creature indeed. If he had a valley filled entirely with gold, all he would want is another valley filled entirely with gold. And nothing fills the stomach of man in the end, except dust.
- The god has not created anything rarer than a good mind. And sometimes I think that good minds are rarer on this Earth than red sulfur.

On the Last Prophet's Wisdom

- There is no poverty worse than ignorance. And there is no wealth greater than a good mind. And there is no loneliness worse than vanity. And there is no family name more honorable than possessing excellent manners. And there is no worship better than quiet meditation [or peaceful thought].

- No two things are more beautiful when put together as when knowledge and humility [or kindness] come together.
- Use four things [in preparation for the next life] before you lose them: use your youth before you lose it, use your health before you lose it, use your wealth before you lose it, and use your life before you lose it.
- Justice is beautiful, but it is more beautiful when found in those with power. Generosity is beautiful, but it is more beautiful when found in those who are rich. Humbleness is beautiful, but it is more beautiful when found in those with knowledge and wisdom. Patience is beautiful, but it is more beautiful when found in those who are poor. Spirituality is beautiful, but it is more beautiful when found in the young. Bashfulness is beautiful, but it is more beautiful when found in women.

PART 2

Are those ingrained in knowledge equal to those who do not know?

39:9

3 The Scientific Enterprise

It's now time to switch gears, so to speak, and start traveling down the intriguing and colorful road of science. Specifically, we'll be touring through more than twenty-five hundred years of past scientific insight and discovery, although this tour will be rather quick and somewhat disconnected. We'll also be attempting to deconstruct the institution of science, the foundations of which have allowed the human species to achieve an impressive degree of understanding of many of nature's basic components, governing forces, and complex interactions. This is an understanding so remarkable and so penetrating—especially given the relatively brief period of time over which it occurred—that we can state with some confidence that the human experience may turn out to be a unique one—possibly within the bounds of the entire known universe!

But before we begin our journey, let me pose a simple yet central question: What exactly is *science*?

Understanding the Nature of Science

The question of what science is almost sounds like a rhetorical one given the degree to which science penetrates our daily lives and the level to which it drives the current state of human affairs. The influence of science grows with every passing day and appears to recognize no barriers. Science, it seems, conquers all, regardless of personal aptitude, geography, ethnicity, culture, age, economic status, social status, political bias, or anything else that may define or differentiate us. I used to think—and to a large extent still think—that science will ultimately shape almost everything around us, including our personal and work habits, our choice of friends, and perhaps even our innermost values and ideals. Science, however, is not some sort of fad or something that only offers pleasure or convenience. Science represents much more—nothing less than fundamental truth.

We'll further explore this aspect of science later in this chapter as well as in chapter 4, but for now let's begin to explore the origins of modern science and how it has progressed since then to our present day. The discussion is by no means a comprehensive history of all of science but instead represents a rather brief summary of the major contributions that have shaped our present scientific landscape. So let's grab our favorite cup of java (or tea) and endeavor to enjoy—and appreciate—our history of science road trip!

A Brief History of Science

Although many natural world discoveries were made by ancient civilizations that predated the Greek civilization, most historians place the birth of modern Western science in ancient Greece approximately twenty-five hundred years ago. This period witnessed the emergence of a number of notable philosopher-scientists, including the famous philosophers Plato (429–347 BCE); Aristotle (384–322 BCE), who was one of Plato's students and a teacher of Alexander the Great; and Archimedes (287–212 BCE), who is generally considered to be one of this period's greatest mathematicians. These philosopher-scientists employed the methods of logic, reason, and mathematics to gain rather broad insights into the workings of our natural world, some of which have remained surprisingly valid today.

For example, Democritus (460–370 BCE) was probably the first to formulate an atomic theory of the cosmos (the Greek word for *universe*). He aptly reasoned that all matter must ultimately be composed of indivisible entities called atoms (or the original Greek *atomos*, which means indivisible). This startling conclusion was scientifically confirmed more than two thousand years later through the work of the physicists John Dalton (1766–1844), J. J. Thomson (1856–1940), and Ernest Rutherford (1871–1937), whose collective work yielded significant insights into the inner structure of the atom and confirmed the atomic theory of matter.

Another example from this period is one we're all familiar with from geometry class: the Pythagorean theorem, named after Pythagoras (570–495 BCE), a famous Greek mathematician and philosopher. Although the geometry of the Pythagorean theorem was known in other parts of the world prior to the Greeks, Pythagoras is the one credited with establishing its *proof*, a notion central to science and its advancement. Pythagoras was also the founder of a mystical religious movement known as Pythagoreanism, which stressed the importance of mathematics in defining the reality of the universe.

A third example of modern scientific theories developed in ancient times is that of the mathematician Euclid of Alexandria, who lived around 300 BCE and who has come to be known as the father of geometry. Euclid was a prolific mathematician who wrote a famous book called the *Elements*, which would go on to become the main geometry textbook used within learning institutions around the world up until the late nineteenth century.[39]

---

39. It is rumored that Euclid was once asked by his ruler if there was an easier way to study geometry other than through the *Elements*. Euclid responded by saying,

All in all, these early Greek philosopher-scientists were responsible for laying the first foundations of the modern scientific enterprise and did so mostly (if not exclusively) through the power of the most complex and wondrous tool in the known universe—the human brain. It would take almost a thousand years before the world would witness yet another similarly powerful scientific awakening.

The next notable chapter in the history of science occurred in southern Europe during the time of the Renaissance (or "rebirth") with the emergence of a group of scientists (mostly astronomers) that included Nicolaus Copernicus (1473–1543), Galileo Galilei (1564–1642), Johannes Kepler (1571–1630), and Tycho Brahe (1546–1601). These scientists are recognized as having made key astronomical discoveries that ultimately led to a vastly different understanding of the celestial (and religious) significance of planet Earth. Before continuing with this chapter in the history of science, though, it's probably worthwhile to pause to briefly describe the important role that Islamic thought and Muslim scientists played in advancing the Western scientific enterprise.

Many science historians believe that the Islamic influence on the advancement of Western science was important in many respects and should not be overlooked. During the period that preceded the European Renaissance, a number of important Muslim scientists emerged across the Middle East and North Africa who made important contributions across a wide spectrum of scientific disciplines, including mathematics, physics, optics, chemistry, and medicine.[40] These scientists played an instrumental role in enabling a transfer of knowledge from the Islamic centers of thought (most notably, from the cities of Baghdad, Cairo, Damascus, and Cordoba) to their European counterparts before the Renaissance occurred.

For instance, one of the most influential Muslim mathematicians of this era was a Persian scientist named Al-Khwarizmi (780–850). Through his systematic approach to solving linear and quadratic equations, Al-Khwarizmi has been credited with greatly advancing algebra, one of the most important branches of pure mathematics (the word *algebra* comes from the Arabic word *Al-Jabr*). In addition to his contributions in algebra and trigonometry, Al-Khwarizmi made significant contributions in the areas of geography, astronomy, and cartography (the study and practice of making maps). Another important scientist of this period was Al-Kindi (801–873), also known as "the Arab philosopher." In addition to being considered an important philosopher, Al-Kindi was an astrologer,

---

"There is no royal road to geometry."

40. In addition to Muslim contributors, the realm of "Islamic" science included many Jewish and Christian scientists and scholars.

an astronomer, a cosmologist, a chemist, a logician, a mathematician, a musician, a physician, a physicist, a psychologist, and a meteorologist.[41] Al-Kindi was also a pioneer in several of the aforementioned scientific disciplines, most notably chemistry and medicine, and has been credited with being one of the fathers of the important field of cryptography, the science of securing sensitive data and a cornerstone of our modern global economy. Within the fields of chemistry and medicine, one of the most important Muslim scientists to emerge during this era was a Persian scientist and philosopher named Ibn Sina (980–1037)—or Avicenna as he's known in the West—who is generally recognized as the father of modern medicine. Avicenna was said to have memorized the entire Quran by the age of ten and wrote hundreds of treatises on various topics, all while also being active in matters of state. In the centuries following his death, his writings in medicine and pharmacology became some of the most influential texts in Europe. Yet another notable Muslim scientist was Al-Haytham (965–1040)—or Alhazen, as he's known in the West—who made key contributions in the fields of optics, engineering, and visual perception, to name a few. He was also known for his early application of the so-called "scientific method" that I'll briefly describe later in this chapter and that constitutes the foundation of our modern science. In fact, Alhazen had become so well known that he was nicknamed both "Ptolemy the second" (the first being a famous scientist who lived in the second century) and "the physicist" in then-medieval Europe.[42]

One of the most important Islamic influences on the development of Western science was in the field of "number theory," a special and bewildering branch of mathematics. Prior to the Renaissance, the Arabic numeral system (the numbering system we use in the West today) was used by Muslim scientists within the areas of the Middle East and North Africa, while the Roman numeral system—an inferior system that limited the ability to carry out some advanced mathematical calculations—was used in Europe. Because of the Arabic system's use of a zero and positional notation, its adoption by Western science constituted a major milestone in the advancement of mathematics in particular and of science in general. In reality, though, the Arabic system did not originate in either the Islamic Middle East or in North Africa but was imported from India. However, it was through Muslim scientists and the Islamic centers of thought that the

---

41. Can you imagine someone holding title to twelve different specialties today?
42. One of those influenced by Alhazen was an English Christian monk named Roger Bacon (1214–1294), who embraced Alhazen's experimental approach and has since been credited as being one of the earliest Europeans to advocate the modern scientific method.

system was slowly adopted in Europe, with clear implications to advancing Western mathematics and Western science.

Summing up the influence of Islam on Western science, perhaps one of the most powerful statements made in recognizing this influence—while specifically calling out the role of the Quran—comes from George Sarton (1884–1956), a prolific science historian and writer, generally recognized as the founder of the history of science as a discipline. As stated in his famous book series *Introduction to the History of Sciences,* Sarton writes that in order to fully conceive the motive behind the fields of science, we should note the axial role of the Quran for them (the merit of this statement will become more obvious after reading chapter 4).[43]

In any event, the second chapter (or third, depending on how you count it) of the history of science was written during the Renaissance, with advances in astronomy that resulted in revising the idea of Earth as the center of the universe—one of the most important scientific discoveries up to that time. As mentioned earlier, one of the key scientists of this period was Galileo, who was also the first human to apply the newly invented telescope to astronomy and who has since been credited with several titles, including that of father of science. The discoveries made by Galileo and other scientists of this period overturned cherished, long-held beliefs and started what can be described as nothing less than a powerful revolution in science.

This "scientific revolution" officially marks the period of time when older, incorrect, medieval concepts were overturned by discoveries made by scientists whose efforts, spanning a period from around 1543 to the late eighteenth century, resulted in reinforcing the foundations of the modern scientific establishment initially laid by the earlier Greek philosopher-scientists some two thousand years prior. One of the most important scientists to emerge toward the later part of this revolution was Sir Isaac Newton (1643–1727). Newton was a gifted scientist of the highest caliber and is considered by many to be one of the most influential people ever to have lived. His work *Philosophiae Naturalis Principia Mathematica* (*Principia* or *Principles* for short), published in 1687, is considered to be one of the most important scientific books ever written, and anyone who has studied physics or basic science should be familiar with Newton's famous laws of motion and gravity. Common folklore even has an apple falling on Newton's head as the inspiration for his theory of gravity. Regardless of the origin of Newton's insight, it's rather amazing how laws discovered more

43. George Sarton, *From Homer to Omar Khayyam,* 5, quoted in Mehdi Golshani, *The Holy Quran and the Sciences of Nature: A Theological Reflection,* 115.

than three hundred years ago are still required study in higher-learning institutions all around the world today.

During the eighteenth and nineteenth centuries, a number of influential mathematicians emerged, and the field of mathematics was correspondingly greatly advanced. In addition to Newton, important mathematicians of this period included Carl Friedrich Gauss (1777–1855), also known as the "prince of mathematicians," Leonhard Euler (1707–1783), and Bernhard Riemann (1826–1866). In many respects, mathematics can be thought of as a foundational domain—the knowledge of which has greatly influenced the subsequent development of the science of physics; this, in turn, has led to advances within the science of chemistry, which has led to advances within the science of biology.

By the mid- to late 1800s, an important stage was set in expanding the sphere of human thought and advancing our modern scientific enterprise. It was at this time that scientists were able to construct specialized, complex scientific instruments housed within dedicated facilities known as laboratories. The advanced instruments within these laboratories provided scientists with the ability to carry out highly accurate measurements (relative to the time period) that expanded the frontier of science into never-seen-before territories that would pave the way for even more impressive scientific discoveries.

Over the next one hundred years or so, humans would go on to build some of the most complex and elaborate scientific instruments ever created, the purpose of which was to gain deep insights into nature and to better understand the composition and interaction of the smallest building blocks of matter that make up our universe. It was also during this time that scientists discovered that matter is ultimately composed of atoms and that atoms were, in turn, composed of smaller elements called electrons, protons, and neutrons. The protons and neutrons were found to reside within what's called the atomic nucleus, while the electrons—although normally bound to the nucleus—exist outside of, and far away from, this nucleus. In fact, matter, it turns out, is made up mostly of empty space.

To better appreciate this intriguing fact, imagine an atom enlarged to the size of a football stadium (atoms are so small that a thread of atoms two inches long contains an atom for every person in the United States). Now further imagine that we place a pin on the ground in this stadium. Well, the head of this pin now corresponds to the nucleus of the atom, while the electrons circle the nucleus from the top of the stadium (close to where the illuminating lights are), and that's how empty matter really is! Now, you may be wondering: Why does a brick feel solid if most of my hand and the brick are empty space? That's because of something called the *electromagnetic force*, one of the four fundamental forces of nature and the force responsible for electricity and magnetism, along with their associated attractive and repellent properties. The electromagnetic force is the same force, for instance, that you feel pushing your hands away if you tried to bring like poles of two magnets together. So, when you're "holding" the brick, your hand atoms are feeling a repellent force from that of the brick atoms. And although you're not *physically* in contact with the brick, you still feel like you're holding something solid, even though there is mostly empty space within the vicinity of your hand and the brick. Of course, a brick feels more solid than water, for example, because brick atoms are "packed" much closer to each other than water atoms are.

As the years went by and human knowledge progressed, scientists continued to build more expensive and elaborate laboratories that included facilities known as particle accelerators. These facilities are large and complex structures that house complicated and extremely sensitive instruments called detectors.[44] Within these accelerators, elementary particles of matter are continuously smashed against each other at incredibly high speeds, yielding even more fundamental atomic components and providing further insights into the true nature of matter. Today, scientists recognize that the most fundamental constituents of matter are called *quarks* and *leptons*. However, they have also speculated that these constituents may not be the "ultimate" building blocks of matter and that even more elementary structures are yet to be discovered. In fact, one of the most exciting theories to have been proposed recently attempts to identify these ultimate building blocks in what is known as string (or superstring) theory. According to string theory, the most fundamental building blocks of matter are nothing more than vibrating strings. These strings vibrate in nine or ten spatial dimensions and one time dimension (in contrast, humans live in a world with three spatial dimensions and one time dimension). These strings are also very, very small. If you can imagine an atom enlarged to the size of our solar system, the nucleus of that atom would correspond to the size of Earth. How large would a single string be in comparison to this Earth-sized nucleus in this new model? It would be no larger than a light bulb! This is why some scientists have said that if we ever wanted to "see" a single string, we would need to build an accelerator the size of an entire galaxy (assuming Congress provides funding, of course). In any case, string theory is just a theory for now, with several more competing theories under consideration.

One of the most advanced accelerators (or *colliders*, as they're also called) built to date is called the Large Hadron Collider (the same "LHC" noted

---

44. To better appreciate the enormity of these inventions, search the Internet for "LHC detectors" and try to find a photo of one with a human included.

earlier), recently completed near the Swiss city of Geneva at a cost of about $10 billion and following an almost fifteen-year construction period. The LHC is said to be *the* most sophisticated and elaborate scientific instrument built by humanity thus far and was referred to as "the pyramids of our time" by one scientist. Scientists hope that the LHC will duplicate the conditions present in the cosmos immediately following the so-called "big bang" (the event that *sparked* the beginning of our universe, which we'll discuss in chapter 5) and provide our species with the deepest levels of insight into the true nature of matter, as well as confirm some of our most fundamental scientific theories.

Returning to our story of science history, one of the most important scientists to emerge in the last hundred years was Albert Einstein (1879–1955). Like Newton, Einstein was an immensely gifted scientist who's been called the father of modern physics and who received the Nobel Prize in 1921.[45] Einstein championed the concept of the "thought experiment," where he wondered what it would be like to ride a beam of light (light being theoretically the fastest thing in the universe). Einstein also corrected Newton in the understanding of some of the most significant elements of our reality, including those of the true nature of "space" and "time." Newton believed that space and time were "absolute," while Einstein demonstrated they are instead "relative" ("absolute time" means that time flows at the same rate everywhere in the universe). As a matter of fact, the concepts of space and time are so elusive that physicists still debate their true fundamental nature today. Einstein also told us, through his famous $E = mc^2$ equation, that matter and energy are interchangeable concepts, and because of that, matter can be converted into energy and energy can be likewise converted into matter. This conversion process is what takes place inside the stars we see in the night sky. Stars continuously convert their matter into energy in the forms of heat and light, as well as produce the outward energy required to prevent the heavy star from collapsing back onto itself (another topic we'll explore in chapter 5). Without this crucial matter-to-energy conversion process, we on Earth would not feel any warmth from our sun, nor would we have any light.

Also during the early twentieth century, a new branch of physics was born called *quantum mechanics*. This area of study came about when the observed results of certain experiments did not agree with the classical laws of physics of the time. Quantum mechanics was thus created in an attempt to provide more accurate (as in better agreement between what physicists calculate and what they measure) insights into nature's fundamental con-

---

45. It may surprise you to learn that he received the prize for his lesser-known work on the photoelectric effect and not for his now-famous theory of relativity.

* conceived of

stituents at the subatomic scale. What has made this field so intriguing, though, is that quantum mechanics is very difficult to understand, (or more appropriately, to visualize) despite its distinct ability to successfully explain the behavior and interactions of nature's most elementary particles. Scientists have since discovered that they simply cannot use everyday accepted notions of reality to describe the special reality of quantum mechanics— nature's *true reality* at the tiniest of scales.

In this sense, quantum mechanics has been also described by scientists as being completely counterintuitive, even verging on the absurd. Many scientists have since given up on the idea of trying to visualize quantum mechanics or what it really "means" and have instead focused on advancing quantum mechanics through the exclusive use of pure mathematical prowess. One scientist, the eloquent and captivating American Nobel Prize physicist Richard Feynman (1918–1988) once remarked, "There was a time when the newspapers said that only twelve men understood the theory of relativity. I do not believe there ever was such a time. There might have been a time when only one man did, because he was the only guy who caught on, before he wrote his paper. But after people read the paper, a lot of people understood the theory of relativity in some way or other, certainly more than twelve. On the other hand, I think I can safely say that nobody understands quantum mechanics."[46]

Nevertheless, the field of quantum mechanics continued to advance and along the way brought to the forefront some of the most brilliant scientists to have ever walked this Earth. In fact, every single one of the nine scientists normally credited with creating quantum mechanics has been awarded the Nobel Prize in Physics at some point in their respective careers! It's also quite amazing that most of these scientists made the impressive advances they made while still in their twenties or early thirties. In this regard, a brilliant but brash scientist by the name of Wolfgang Pauli (1900–1958), also a quantum mechanics pioneer, once scorned an assistant of his (who would go on to become a leading physics theorist) by saying, "So young and already you are unknown." Pauli is also known to have once remarked when reviewing the paper of another physicist, "This isn't right. This isn't even wrong."[47]

---

46. Feynman, *Character*.

47. I too, have my own story related to quantum mechanics: During my college years, I became interested in quantum mechanics and enrolled in a course taught by a knowledgeable and kind-hearted older professor. Most of the grading was based on a midterm and a final exam, with 10 percent of the grade allocated for class interaction, which we all "aced" since no one really understood the subject and we all asked lots of questions. We had more problems with the midterm, though. We were stunned by how difficult the exam was, as evidenced by our average score of

The science of physics continued to build on the ideas of quantum mechanics and new discoveries and continued to advance until about the 1970s with the culmination of what's called "the standard model." This theory is, in the minds of many physicists, humanity's "pride and joy" in achieving the most intimate levels of understanding of our natural world. The success of this theory, in terms of the demonstrated agreement between calculation and measurement, has been nothing short of absolutely phenomenal. Nonetheless, the standard model is not considered to be a "theory of everything," and many prominent physicists are diligently working today on proving such a theory—if in fact one exists (one of the candidates for such a theory is string theory).

Advances within the science of physics have driven advances within the science of chemistry. One of the greatest milestones within chemistry was the creation of what's known as the periodic table of the elements. The brilliant Russian scientist and professor of chemistry Dmitri Mendeleev (1834–1907) first proposed this organization of chemical elements. He grouped chemical elements together based on a common set of repeating properties (hence the name *periodic*). Mendeleev also predicted the existence of yet unknown elements, which, when later discovered, confirmed his insights and established the periodic table as a cornerstone for the future development of chemistry.[48] The periodic table, a required topic in any entry-level chemistry course today, beautifully illustrates how everything in nature, from soap to a watermelon to the largest star, is made up of a

---

27 out of 100 (believe me, that's bad). When the professor walked in to hand us our individual scores, he was utterly depressed and at a loss for words. He apologized profusely, saying that this was the first time he taught undergraduates and that he didn't realize how different (i.e., intellectually inferior) we were from graduate students. He promised to give us a makeup exam "fit for undergrads" and asked us to not let this ego-destroying calamity keep us from enjoying the rest of our natural lives. Unfortunately, though, the makeup turned out to be even more difficult than the midterm. We became certain of this when we came out of class and were handed the exam answers. We gathered, offered our "condolences" to one another, and looked at the answers. Then we started to laugh and joked to each other that not only did we not understand the exam questions, but we couldn't even understand the answers!

48. Mendeleev's intellectual curiosity was so broad and impressive that he was called "the Russian Leonardo da Vinci." Mendeleev's account of his insight into the periodic table of elements is also quite fascinating: On the night of February 17, 1869, after staying up for three days and three nights laboring over how to group the chemical elements in some meaningful way, he had an extraordinary dream, in which the chemical elements appeared to fall into a table "as required," confirming his suspicion that elements ultimately fit into specific groupings based upon repeating properties.

rather small number of essential building blocks, called elements. Imagine all the things in the universe, including everything ever made by man, and realize that this great multitude of diverse things all boil down to a mere hundred or so chemical elements! Each of these elements is referred to by an alphabetical designation of one to three letters, and each maintains a distinct set of physical and chemical properties that uniquely identifies it. As a matter of fact, scientists discovered that it was through the laws of quantum mechanics that chemical elements take on the individual chemical identities they do through what's known as the "Pauli exclusion principle" (yes, named after the same curious scientist we just met).[49]

The most remarkable theory in biology was published in 1859, just prior to these advances in physics and chemistry. The theory of evolution by Charles Darwin (1809–1882) is so profound that some have referred to it as the most important scientific insight made within the "entirety of human thought." The process of natural selection, as it's called, has demonstrated how life evolved and continues to evolve on Earth. It has also confirmed life to have a common origin, something we'll learn more about in chapter 7. After Darwin's theory of evolution, a second "revolution" within the science of biology occurred in the early 1950s with the discovery of deoxyribonucleic acid (also known as DNA) by James Watson (born 1928) and Francis Crick (1916–2004), both of whom were awarded the Nobel Prize for their discovery of the "secret of life." This powerful revolution has continued into our present day and aims to better understand the components and interactions of the biological building blocks of life. These efforts normally fall under the current fields of molecular biology and genetic engineering and hold great promise for the medical field in the treatment of many different types of human diseases and abnormalities. A striking example of one of the more recent efforts related to DNA research has been the human genome project, which began in 1990 and which aims to one day decipher the structure and functionality of the entire genetic makeup of the human species.

Within the science of geology, two important discoveries must be highlighted. The first took place in the late nineteenth and early twentieth centuries and pertains to discovering the real age (or an accurate approximation) of Earth, as Earth was found to be much older than was previously thought. The second key discovery is the theory of plate tectonics,

---

49. Another important scientist who contributed to our knowledge of chemical elements was a French nobleman named Antoine-Laurent de Lavoisier (1743–1794), who is recognized today as the "Isaac Newton of chemistry" and the father of modern chemistry. He was also the first scientist to put together an extensive list of chemical elements.

advanced during the middle part of the twentieth century. Plate tectonics posits that Earth's crust is made up of many "plates" and that these plates move horizontally as they're driven by heat energy from Earth's interior. The implication of this theory had, and continues to have, a significant effect on the beginning and evolution of life on planet Earth, something we'll explore in more detail in chapter 6.

Within the science of cosmology, important advances took place in the beginning of the twentieth century and continue today. Some notable developments within this science include the big bang theory, the theory of cosmic inflation, the discovery of the expansion of the universe, and the discovery of dark matter and dark energy. It turns out that most of our universe is made of dark matter and dark energy. Everything else—including us and other forms of matter we can normally "see," such as planets, stars, and galaxies—constitutes only 4 percent of the total, with the balance (96 percent) being the "dark stuff," the nature of which scientists still do not understand. Breakthroughs in cosmology have also been coupled with (and at times partly as a result of) the construction of complex scientific instruments, such as state-of-the-art telescopes, to see farther into the night sky. Some of these instruments, which sometimes even orbit Earth in outer space, are designed to observe distant celestial objects located billions of light-years away (a light-year is the distance traveled by light in one year, equivalent to almost six trillion miles). In fact, some of the most beautiful images of some faraway places in our universe have come from the Hubble space telescope, named after the American astronomer Edwin Hubble (1889–1953) and launched into Earth's orbit in 1990.

All of this knowledge and associated scientific advancements—enabled exclusively through science and mathematics—along with its influence on human civilization and the broader human condition, will undoubtedly continue for as long as we remain a viable species. In many respects, you can even argue that the discovery of our natural world is probably just beginning. And who knows what exciting secrets and mysteries the universe and future hold in store for us?

The Foundations of Science

Let's now try to explore the question of why science has proven to be so successful in providing our species with so much insight into the secrets and mysteries of the natural world. What, let us ask, has set science apart from other failed knowledge-seeking endeavors that, although popular within certain times or geographies, have nonetheless failed the test of time and have become—outside of a passing mention in a few history books—completely forgotten? Why does science represent "real and concrete knowledge," whereas other endeavors represent myths, fallacies, superstitions, and folklore? Why can we even propose that science may very well represent a class of truth or even a form of virtue when such honor cannot be bestowed upon other areas of human thought and venture?[50]

To begin to properly address such questions, we must first recognize that science has become special among all other thought- and knowledge-seeking efforts precisely because of the foundations or principles through which science has come to be known as science. These guiding precepts are faithfully adhered to by all science practitioners regardless of a scientist's field of study, place of origin, particular affiliation, or time period. In fact, one can argue that it is *only* through these principles that science has achieved, and continues to hold, its unique status as inarguable knowledge.

We must therefore seek to shed light on these fundamental codes of conduct and endeavor to further explore their meaning and significance if we want to satisfactorily answer the questions posed thus far. I will not attempt to provide an exhaustive discussion of all the principles of science here but will instead focus on the most important ones—perhaps the only ones worth considering. And although these principles can be stated differently or more elaborately, their essential meaning nevertheless remains the same.

I propose (or, more appropriately, I think of science as built upon) five such principles, which together constitute the intellectual structure of the institution of science:
- Principle I: Observation
- Principle II: Thoughtfulness
- Principle III: Eagerness and Ability to Learn New Knowledge
- Principle IV: Eagerness and Ability to Question and Refute Existing Knowledge
- Principle V: Proof Seeking

Principle I: Observation

It's hard to think of any scientific theory or breakthrough that did not involve observation. We are, after all, an integral part to our environment, exist within it, and are shaped by it, and any understanding of this environment requires the simple act of observing it.

Principle II: Thoughtfulness

It's equally difficult to conceive of any scientific advancement without the principle of thoughtfulness. In science, thoughtfulness is the process by

---

50. Although I do not get into them here, you may want to research the now forgotten but once popular fields of phrenology and the science of spiritualism to better appreciate the motive behind these questions.

which we attempt to achieve a good understanding of a particular event, phenomenon, problem, or issue. This understanding usually entails the proper formulation of the experimental design, a careful analysis of the experiment, determination of a set of results and conclusions, and finally a test of the validity of the conclusions reached. Thoughtfulness may, and usually does, include a combination of efforts, such as those of rational thought, thought experiments, mathematical reasoning and manipulation, and peer reviews and discussion. Scientists use the principle of thoughtfulness in combination with the principles of observation and proof seeking to propose, modify, or overturn a scientific theory or proposition.

Principle III: Eagerness and Ability to Learn New Knowledge

It should come as no surprise that knowledge is a key component of science. One of the main reasons (if not *the* main reason) scientists "do science" is to gain, enhance, or update scientific knowledge. Moreover, our present view of a scientist is that of a person who has learned a great deal, as one must have typically earned the equivalent of bachelor's, master's, and doctoral degrees to even qualify for holding the title of "scientist" today. In addition, our view of a scientist is that of a person who possesses a strong innate drive to know and ample ambition to increase and constantly refresh that base of knowledge.

Principle IV: Eagerness and Ability to Question and Refute Existing Knowledge

Equally important to the drive to learn new knowledge is the drive to question and discredit existing knowledge and "accepted" facts. As new discoveries are made, scientists use newly obtained data to examine accepted standard beliefs. If and when fresh data do not agree with an existing framework, a new framework—regardless of how difficult that change may seem—is established and adopted by science. Some of humanity's greatest scientists, including Galileo, Darwin, and Einstein, have become famous because they questioned and successfully overturned long-held, cherished beliefs.

Principle V: Proof Seeking

Simply put, a scientific proposition must be subject to the rigor of proof before it can be accepted and adopted by the wider scientific community. After all, proof *is* what constitutes the truth component of science. Within the general realm of science, true statements are accepted as either axioms or must be provable.[51] And only when irrefutable proof is established— ∼

---

51. An axiom is a universally accepted or self-evident truth, such as this statement:

proof that reflects the truthfulness of the proposed idea or theory—can scientific acceptance be granted (although the specific method of proof or validation is usually not the same among various areas of knowledge or even among various disciplines within the same science).

The Scientific Method

In addition to these five principles of science, science has also become science because it concerns itself only with that which is observable, measurable, and testable. The actual term that officially describes such a framework is called the *scientific method*, which is a framework that is based on systematically observing, measuring, and experimenting, as well as a method for formulating, testing, and modifying scientific hypotheses. Because of science's reliance on the scientific method, the "type" of knowledge that science seeks to uncover and explain is limited only to that which is in complete compliance with this scientific method.

Many have argued that scientific truths represent a higher order of Truth than that of religious or spiritual truths because the claims made by science are measurable, testable, and provable.[52] On the other hand, religious (or spiritual) truths—with the highest truth being the existence of a supreme being or an intelligent and overwhelming universal order—cannot be measurable, testable, or provable. In a rather unusual way, however, this book attempts to prove the highest religious (or spiritual) truth from the truths of science. Stated differently, this book argues that if we accept the truth of established science as one axiom and that only through the divine can such science (or scientific insight) be foretold as a second axiom, and if we further agree with and accept the arguments and reasoning presented in Part 3 of this book, then we must acknowledge the highest religious (or spiritual) truth: the existence of the Supreme Being.

---

if Mark is 5 feet tall, and Lisa is 5 feet tall, then Mark and Lisa are the same height.

52. Some readers may object to equating spirituality with religion. While such an objection is generally valid, I nonetheless assume the existence of a supreme being or overwhelming and intelligent universal order to constitute a spiritual truth.

4 Science and the Quran— Key Similarities

In the previous chapter, I introduced the principles of science and suggested that it was because of these principles that science can be thought of as representing a class of truth or, if like me, you believe that truth and virtue are strongly related, perhaps even a form of virtue. In this chapter, I propose that the same principles that govern the realm of science are surprisingly similar to the principles underlying the Quran. I will therefore demonstrate what I believe to be a remarkable similarity between the spirit or essence of science and that of the Quran.

But first, allow me to engage your imagination.

Let's assume that you're a non-Arabic speaker but that somehow, perhaps magically, you wake up tomorrow morning completely fluent in Arabic. Let's further imagine that you decided that the first thing you want to do with your newfound knowledge is read the Quran. Let's also assume that you possessed the patience and stamina required to read the entire Quran, cover to cover, in a single sitting (theoretically possible but certainly difficult to achieve).

What would strike you the most about the Quran in such a circumstance? What curious or peculiar aspect of the Quran would stand out and leave a deep and lasting impression on you?

Naturally, different people would most likely come up with different answers to these questions, given their diverse backgrounds and varying levels of knowledge and linguistic abilities—beauty is in the eye of the beholder, after all. In spite of this apparent difference, however, I believe that we will find a common theme that resonates with most of us: the Quran's extensive use of the same principles outlined in chapter 3, the principles that characterize and sustain the institution of science.

This belief is why I decided to dedicate a separate chapter to present and argue the parallels between science and the Quran, an assertion you may find surprising or perhaps even nonsensical. If I convince you, however, and you end up accepting my proposition, then an important follow-up question should come to mind: Why do these parallels exist? I'll explore a plausible answer to this question as well before moving on to specific science and verse comparisons in Part 3.

In the next few pages, I present a limited sample of verses and sets of verses that embody the common principles between science and the Quran. Of course, I did not list all the verses of the Quran that embody these common principles, primarily because of space and because such a comprehensive list falls outside of this book's primary purpose. Instead, I have opted to focus on a select set of verses, with each demonstrating one or more of the principles in support of my overall argument. I therefore ask that you consider the overall set to be much larger and assure you that the principles they speak to permeate the entire Quran.[53] Let's now begin to examine these verses:

> Or who created the heavens and Earth, and brought down
> water from the sky, so we [the god] sprung through it beautiful
> [or awe-inspiring] gardens, the likes of which you [humanity]
> were unable to create. So is there a god besides the god? But
> they deviate from the truth. Or who made Earth a calm [or
> restful] place, and made rivers run through her, and gave
> her anchors,[54] and made a barrier between the two seas. So
> is there a god besides the god? But most of them [people] do
> not have knowledge. Or who answers the prayer of who is in
> dire need, and alleviates pain, and makes you later ones.[55] So
> is there a god besides the god? But little do you [humanity]
> study [or remember]. Or who guides you in the darkness of
> the land and the sea, and who sends the winds to give you joy
> from within [or prior to] his [the god's] mercy. So is there a god
> besides the god? Elevated is he from the gods they call. Or who
> starts life and then later restarts it, and who feeds you from the
> sky and the earth [or land]. So is there a god besides the god?
> [to Muhammad] Say to them, "Show me your proof if you
> indeed stand for the truth."
>
> (27:60–64)
>
> Indeed, in the:
> Creation of the heavens and Earth,
> And the changing of the night and day,
> And the ships that travel in the oceans to benefit people,

---

53. These claims can be independently verified by examining a translated Quran.
54. Chapter 6 provides a detailed discussion of "anchors."
55. Chapter 7 provides a discussion of "later ones."

*And what the god has brought down from the sky as water so
he breathed life into a dead land,
And the movers [or creatures] on Earth [or the land],
And the driving of the winds and the clouds for a useful
purpose,
Are clear signs for a mindful [or intelligent, thoughtful] people.*

(2:164)

*And the god brought down from the sky water, so he gave life
to the land after she had died. In this is a sign for a people who
listen. And there is a lesson for you [humanity] in the cattle.
We [the god] give you from within their insides, from between
blood and waste, pure milk tasty for the drinkers. And from the
fruits of palm trees and the grapes, you use to make wines and
good foods. Surely, in this is a sign for a mindful [or intelligent,
thoughtful] people.*

(16:65–67)

*Do they not see [or observe, contemplate] how the camel's were
created?
And how the sky was erected?
And how the mountains were firmly laid?
And how the earth [or land] was made plain?*

(88:17–20)

*He [the god] is the one who brought down from the sky water,
some you drink, and some you irrigate and eat from your
plants. With it [water], he [the god] causes vegetation to spring
for your [humanity's] benefit: olives, palms, grapes, and all
kinds of fruits. Surely, in these are signs for people who think.
And he [the god] put to your [humanity's] use [or benefit] the
night and the day, and the sun and the moon, and the stars are
made to benefit you through his will [or command]. Surely, in
all of this are clear signs [or matters to contemplate and reflect
upon] for mindful [or intelligent, thoughtful] people. And what
he created [or made, sowed] for you in Earth [or the land]
of varying colors. Surely, in all of this is a sign for those who
reflect. And he is the one who put the sea to your use, so you
eat from it soft flesh and you extract jewelry you wear, and you
[Muhammad] see the ships through the waves, and so that you
[humanity] seek benefits, hoping you are thankful. And he set
on the earth [or land] anchors, so that she does not sway with*

*them, and rivers, and pathways, hoping you find your ways.
And guideposts, and through the stars they find their ways. So
is the one who creates equal to that which does not create? Do
you [humanity] not study [or reflect upon] this?*

(16:10–17)

*Did they not ponder within themselves that the god did not
create the heavens and Earth, and all in between, except
through [or by] Haqq and until a predetermined time? And
surely, a great multitude of people are in complete denial about
meeting their life giver.*

(30:8)

*And of his [the god's] signs is that he created for you
[humanity], like yourselves, mates, so that you find comfort [or
peace] and [the god] enabled between you love and compassion
[or sympathy]. Surely, in these are signs for a thoughtful people.*

(30:21)

*[to Muhammad] Say, "Who is the life giver of the heavens
and Earth?" Say [or answer], "The god." Say, "So you took [or
followed] beneath him [the god] helpers [or friends] who can
neither benefit nor harm themselves?"
Say [or ask], "Are the blind equal to those who see? Or is
darkness equal to light? Or did the gods [or friends] they
assume create as the god created, and the two creations seemed
the same to them?" Say, "The god is the creator of everything,
the one and only, and whose force [or power] is completely
overwhelming."*

(13:16)

*[to Muhammad] Say [or ask], "Can any of the ones you equate
with the god guide to Haqq?" Say [or answer], "The god
guides to Haqq." Is the one who guides to Haqq not worthy to
be followed [or listened to]? Or is he who does not guide [to
Haqq] except that he requires guidance [worthy]? What is your
matter? How do you judge [or decide]? And most of them do
not follow except that which is uncertain [or conjecture]. And
surely, uncertainty [or conjecture] does not suffice for Haqq in
the least.*

(10:35–36)

Is he [the god] who created the heavens and Earth not capable of creating their likes [referring to the resurrection]? Yes! And he is the constant [or continuous] creator, who is filled with knowledge.

(36:81)

Did they not see that the god who created the heavens and Earth, and who did not tire because of this creation, that he is capable of bringing life to the dead? Yes! And he is certainly capable of everything.

(46:33)

And if they [those who opposed the new faith] are told to follow that which the god has brought down [the Quran], they say, "But we follow what we are accustomed to in the ways of our fathers." [They do so] even if their fathers were not at all mindful [or intelligent], nor would they [the fathers] be able to find the right way?

(2:170)

They [idols] are but mere names you and your fathers have named, which the god has not given any power [or authority] to. They [those who opposed the new faith] surely follow only that which is uncertain [or conjecture], and what they desire. But surely, what has come forth from their life giver is the right guidance [or enlightenment].

(53:23)

[to Muhammad] Say, "My life giver has only forbidden the ugly deeds, apparent and concealed, and [forbidden] wrongdoings and aggression without due [or just] cause, and [forbidden] equating with the god that which he has not empowered [or given authority to], and [forbidden] that you [humanity] say about [or attribute to] the god what you have no firm knowledge of."

(7:33)

And if you [Muhammad] follow [or submit to] most who live on Earth, they will cause you to lose the way to [or of] the god. For they only follow [or listen to] uncertainty [or conjecture] and they follow only that which is hearsay.

(6:116)

*And we [the god] directed [or asked] that you [humanity] treat
your parents well [or with kindness]. And should they ask
that you to equate with the god that which you have no firm
knowledge of, do not follow. To me [the god] you [humanity]
shall all return, and I will inform you of all that you have done.*

(29:8)

*And of the people are those who discuss [or debate] the
existence [or nature] of the god without knowledge, or
guidance, or an enlightened book.*

(22:8)

*And as you [humanity] let [words] loose through your tongues,
and your mouths utter what you have no firm knowledge of.
And you [humanity] think lightly of this [or as insignificant],
but it is of great importance to the god [or taken very seriously
by the god].*

(24:15)

*And do not attempt to judge [or decide] based on what you
[humanity] have no firm knowledge of. Surely, the [senses of]
hearing, seeing, and intuition [or wisdom] will all be called to
account [or humanity will be responsible for].*

(17:36)

*And of his [the god's] signs is the creation of the heavens and
Earth, and your [humanity's] varying tongues and colors.
Surely, in these are clear signs to those with much knowledge.*

(30:22)

*And they ask you [Muhammad] about the soul [or spirit,
essence]. Say [or answer], "The soul is my life giver's matter [or
concern], and the knowledge you [humanity] have been given
is only very little."*

(17:85)

Comparison between the Verses and the Essence of Science

It's quite clear from these verses that the Quran urges the important acts
of observation, mindfulness, critical thinking, proper reasoning, study,
reflection, asking questions, and seeking proof. These verses also point to

the importance of acquiring knowledge, especially firm knowledge, along with the importance of seeking clarity in understanding. They encourage the need to question one's ways and traditions, thus avoiding a blind following of these traditions if they are found not to be based on firm knowledge or enlightenment. Some verses further point to the responsibility and criticality of the human senses, as they constitute the means by which we observe and communicate. One of the important concepts that appears several times within these verses is that of Haqq, the concept we initially learned about in chapter 1 and the Arabic word for something that is true, right, fair, or proper. The verses illustrate how this concept lies far above that of uncertainty or conjecture and that the only way to true enlightenment is through Haqq.

Another theme that is exemplified throughout the Quran is found in the verses encouraging readers to engage their mental faculties and *think*. Within many of its verses, the Quran urges its readers to think about the important concepts cited within the Quran. These concepts include belief in the existence of what we know as a supreme being; that the meaning of the human existence cannot be fully understood without observing and contemplating what we hear, see, and feel around us; that all of us are responsible and will be held accountable for our actions; that the purpose of this life is to strive toward attaining the next; and that virtue is the only measure by which we are allowed to differentiate ourselves from each other or from any other forms of life.

As promised in the introduction to this chapter, I'll now attempt to answer the question of why these parallels between science and the Quran even exist. Is there something special about these principles that perhaps points to a deeper quest or truth? And if so, what could this core objective be? In my mind at least, these parallels exist because both science and the Quran seek the same end or, as I alluded to in the beginning of the chapter, the same deeper truth: knowledge.

Science, on the one hand, seeks knowledge of the natural universe. Scientists want to understand how the world we live in works in terms of its natural laws and its fundamental components. We've also come to discover that these laws constitute rules of governance that drive the existence and evolution of our natural environment and, to a large degree, everything within it. Therefore, the knowledge that science seeks to uncover is concrete (as in verifiable and repeatable) and real (as in leading to more fundamental truths). Science has taught us that to uncover this knowledge along with these deeper truths, we need to adhere to the principles of science and abide by the scientific method. There are no shortcuts.

The Quran, too, primarily seeks to discover knowledge. However, the knowledge the Quran seeks to uncover is much broader than that of pure science. The "environment," according to the Quran, is not only the immediate, sensible natural environment around us but also an environment that encompasses the entirety of the human experience. Why are we here? How did we come to be? What is our purpose? Where are we going? What else is out there? What is the god? What is "ultimate knowledge"? All of these represent important questions the Quran is concerned with either answering or raising. However, answers to these questions, as well as to many others, can only be sought and properly understood through knowledge—real and concrete knowledge.

As is true for science, the Quran seems to point to that fact that acquiring such real and concrete knowledge can only be achieved through a set of unshakable principles. And here, too, we have no shortcuts. We are required to observe, think, reason, question, use our senses, understand, seek proof, and revere Haqq. Indeed, the importance of the concept of knowledge to both the Quran and the prophet cannot be overstressed.

Equally important, however, is that we must also recognize the strict limits imposed on our ability to know, as was clearly illustrated in the last sample verse. We must therefore accept that our human knowledge perhaps constitutes only a small subset of a much larger domain of knowledge "out there," and because of this, our comprehension of "true reality" (or how things really are) is either nonexistent or otherwise severely impaired (a point I'll return to later in the book).56

---

56. Even though I am not a scientist and even though knowledge is a rather abstract idea, I suspect that knowledge may prove to play a fundamental role in our existence; it may be very close to what constitutes the ultimate building block of our physical, and perhaps even metaphysical, reality. For instance, one manifestation of this knowledge in biological systems is in our genetic code. If each of us had the exact same code, we would probably be very similar to each other. Such a manifestation of knowledge seems to take place everywhere and at every level of existence. Our universe, I've come to accept, is nothing but a vast warehouse of knowledge (of which domains such as information science and mathematics are subsets).

PART 3

We will show them [humanity] our signs in the future and within themselves, until they realize that he [the god] is the Haqq.

41:53

5 Astronomy and Cosmology

Now that we have a greater understanding of the Quran, Muhammad's mission and character, and the essence and history of science, it's time to delve into how these topics interrelate. Overall, we'll be exploring more than thirty different areas of science that span a wide and rich spectrum of human knowledge and discovery. Within each topic, I'll start by providing an overview of a scientific discovery, followed by the verses from the Quran that relate to that particular discovery. I'll conclude with a discussion aimed at illustrating the agreement between the science and the Quran.

We begin with this chapter, where we explore the fascinating science within two closely related fields: astronomy and cosmology. As you may already know, the science of astronomy is primarily concerned with studying the night sky and its many celestial objects, including objects such as stars, planets, comets, and galaxies. It's also considered to be one of the oldest of the sciences, having been faithfully practiced (and relied upon) by virtually every ancient civilization. The science of cosmology, on the other hand, is a relatively new science and is primarily concerned with the study of the cosmos in its totality. Cosmology includes the study of how the universe came to be, how it evolved since its creation, and how it will continue to progress through the far-distant future.

The Expansion of the Universe

One of the most important discoveries made in cosmology within the last hundred years was the discovery that our universe is expanding, or becoming larger and larger with the progression of time. Also, within about the last thirty years or so, scientists discovered that the universe not only is expanding, but that it's expanding at an accelerated rate (meaning that the rate of expansion is speeding up).

As I mentioned in the Background and Introduction, the verse on the expansion of the universe was one of the key verses that pushed me toward achieving a better understanding of the science of the Quran. This was mostly due to the verse's clarity, simplicity, and inflexible interpretation, as is illustrated below:

> *And the sky we [the god] built with [or through] hands, and we*
> *are surely expanding [or enlarging].*
>
> (51:47)

Let's begin by examining some of the key words used in the verse to better appreciate how they relate to the universe's expansion. The first is *sky*. The Arabic word for *sky* (*sema'a*: "sky, blue heavens, firmament")[57] is normally used to refer to "what's above," since the root of *sema'a*, *sema*, means "to ascend." Thus, *sema'a* can mean Earth's upper atmosphere, distant stars, faraway planets, and the like. In this case, however, I propose that *sema'a* refers to everything we see when we look up at the night sky—the entire universe. The rationale for this interpretation is rather straightforward. As mentioned in chapter 3, one of the most intriguing scientific instruments ever built is a special telescope that orbits Earth, the Hubble space telescope (named after the same astronomer who first discovered that the universe is expanding). Because this telescope orbits in Earth's outer atmosphere, it is located "on Earth" but literally "sees" the deepest regions of our universe. Thus, the presumption that sky can refer to the entire universe in this case is not that farfetched. We have to remember that the Quran was revealed more than fourteen hundred years ago to a rather primitive people. Clearly, there was no concept of *universe* then, at least not to the degree to which we understand or define the concept today. The Quran therefore uses rather simplistic terms to refer to potentially complex phenomena and will at times reuse the same word to refer to quite different things, as was noted in chapter 1.[58]

The next key words we want to study are *with hands* (*be'aydin*: "with, through, by means of hands"), but I'll first need to make an important clarification—one that I'll repeat in other places in the book. It's been firmly established, based upon the Quran and the teachings of the prophet Muhammad, that the god cannot be thought of as possessing hands, legs, lips, or any other human attribute. The god must also be understood not to be bound by space or time or confined in any other conceivable way. The Quran substantiates this "description" through verse 42:11, which states that "*nothing* is even like him [the god]." If we accept the god's lack of any physical attributes, then what does *with hands* actually mean?

---

57. Unless stated otherwise, all translations provided are based on the dictionary *Al-Mawrid*, which is generally considered the most accurate and comprehensive Arabic-English dictionary.

58. A further example of the different meanings of *sema'a* will be provided in chapter 10 when we discuss the "airplane verse," which also uses *sky*. In that verse, *sema'a* specifically refers to an airplane or similar flying machine.

A clue to better understand *with hands* comes from the Quran's discussion of the prophet Dawood (the biblical King David) in verse 38:17. In that verse, the Quran uses "hands" in a similarly abstract sense and associates that usage with King David possessing unusual strength and power. Today, we understand that our universe came into existence through the big bang, a tremendous event that marked the birth of our universe 13.7 billion years ago, during which unbelievably gargantuan levels of power and energy were released.[59] We can thus see how *with hands* can refer to the tremendous power and energy that characterized the beginning of our universe.

The next key word we want to focus on is *expanding* [or *enlarging*] (*musi'oon*: "expanding, widening, broadening, enlarging"). In addition to its obvious meaning as an expansion or enlargement, *musi'oon* implies "a volume," because the root of *musi'oon*, *se'a*, means a capacity to "hold" or "be filled" by something. Through this choice of word, the verse thus seems to imply that this expansion is three-dimensional, further supporting the claim that what this verse describes is the expansion of the universe.

Throughout my Quranic research, I have discovered that the Quran uses specific, precisely chosen words and that one must always pay attention to the particular word choice if one intends to achieve a more in-depth understanding of what the Quran is trying to communicate. Hopefully, you'll come to agree with this assertion by the time you finish reading Part 3.

The Force of Gravity

The force of gravity is the force responsible for keeping us "attached" to Earth. In fact, if someone was to suddenly turn gravity off, we would all fly immediately into space at one thousand miles per hour (twice that of a cruising jetliner). Gravity is one of the four fundamental forces of nature with the other three being the electromagnetic force, the strong nuclear force, and the weak nuclear force. However, the force of gravity is special because it is so unbelievably weak compared to the other three forces. To really comprehend this, notice how you can effortlessly pick up a metal pin from the floor using a small magnet. The magnet grabs the pin because of the attractive nature of the electromagnetic force present between the two objects (this force can also be repellent). In so doing, the tiny pin-magnet pair is going against the opposing gravitational pull of the entire planet on the pin and winning! Because of its relatively weak nature, the force of gravity (which is always attractive) only becomes significant when acting upon very large and massive objects, such as moons, planets, stars, and

---

59. Imagine the entire universe with all its hundreds of billions of planets, stars, and galaxies shrunk to the size of a single atom, and you'll begin to appreciate how energetic this initial state really was.

galaxies. For instance, it's because of gravity that our moon remains in close proximity to Earth, Earth remains part of the solar system (due to Earth's attraction to the sun), and our entire Milky Way galaxy maintains an independent existence from other galaxies with its 200 or so billion stars, all constantly attracted to each other through the force of gravity.

Because the force of gravity is always attractive, it cannot be the only force in play here; otherwise the moon would fall into Earth and Earth would fall into the sun. Luckily, such unfortunate events do not happen because Earth and the moon are in constant motion, and objects that are in motion, specifically rotational motion, also experience a "centrifugal force" that opposes the force of gravity and prevents objects from falling into each other.[60] Newton discovered the law of gravity in the seventeenth century, more than one thousand years after these three verses were revealed:

> *[The god] created the skies without a beam [or pillar] that you [humanity] can see.*
>
> (31:10)

> *The god is the one who erected the skies without a beam [or pillar] that you [humanity] can see.*
>
> (13:2)

> *By the sky that is woven tightly together.*
>
> (51:7)

As we've done in the previous section, let's focus on the key words in these verses. The first is *skies*. This word, *semawat*, is the plural form of the word *sky* we met in the previous section. The first two verses talk about how the *skies* (again, I propose that here *sky* means the larger universe) contain *beams* or *pillars* (*ah'medin*: "columns, pillars, poles, posts, piers") but that these supporting structures cannot be seen by us. These verses clearly allude to something akin to an invisible force present in the grander universe and through which celestial objects are prevented from falling into each other. It's also curious that the verses specifically use *beams* or *pillars* because that implies that objects in the sky are innately driven to fall into each other but cannot (because of the beams' or pillars' presence), similar to how the force of gravity is a naturally attractive force but is opposed by the centrifugal force arising from an object as a result of its rotational

---

60. Centrifugal force is what's known as a fictitious force, invented to allow physicists to do proper "bookkeeping" in a non-inertial frame of reference (a couple of aspirins are recommended if you really want to understand what this means).

motion. The third verse furthermore states that the sky is *woven tightly together* (*thaat el-hubuk*: "interwoven, interlaced, intertwined"[61]), which agrees with our current understanding of how the force of gravity keeps objects tightly bound together and keeps that which is "woven together" from separating.

Stellar and Planetary Orbits

One of the most important insights gained by astronomers in the seventeenth century was that heavenly bodies, such as planets and stars, move in well-defined orbits based upon a set of newly discovered natural laws. These laws include the laws of planetary motion discovered by Kepler, as well as Newton's law of universal gravitation and Newton's laws of motion. The Quran has alluded to these laws through the following verse:

> *It is not appropriate for the sun to reach [or grasp] the moon, nor does the night precede the day, and all swims in its own orbit [or path].*
>
> (36:40)

The verse makes reference to how heavenly bodies, such as the sun and moon, follow individual *orbits* (*felek*: "orbit, circuit"). And although only the sun and moon are listed in the beginning of the verse, the verse uses the word *all* (*kul'lin*: "all, each, every") instead of "both" to describe them in the later part of the verse, most likely to communicate the fact that the sun and moon are just examples and that *swimming in its own orbit* applies to all heavenly bodies, in agreement with the discoveries made by Kepler and Newton.

There is another important point I need to make about this verse. Although one will not find mathematical equations in the Quran and despite the fact that the regularity of heavenly bodies was observed prior to the revelation of the Quran, it's fairly obvious from the verse's choice of words that it is communicating a strong sense of regularity for these heavenly bodies, and that this regularity cannot be violated, in agreement with what we've come to know as natural laws.

The Motion of Earth

For quite a long time, humans believed that Earth was fixed at the center the universe, while all other celestial bodies, including the sun, moon, and stars, devotedly revolved around it. In fact, every time I think about this, I wonder how anyone could think otherwise, as everything does seem to

---

61. Chapter 6 provides an in-depth discussion of the meaning of *thaat*.

rotate around us from our perspective. However, the work of Copernicus and Galileo showed that Earth was the object that rotated around the sun.[62]
As was the case with stellar and planetary orbits, this discovery was made long after the following verse was revealed:

> *And you [Muhammad] see the mountains, thinking they*
> *are fixed, yet they pass as clouds do. [This is] the making [or*
> *endeavoring, manufacturing] of the god who made everything*
> *in an excellent fashion [or in a skillful manner].*
>
> (27:88)

The key word in this verse is *fixed* (*ja'meda*: "solid, rigid, inflexible, immobile, stationary"). The verse states that mountains, although appearing fixed to observers on Earth, are in motion just as clouds are constantly moving. Because mountains are clearly attached to Earth, this verse also seems to imply that Earth as a whole is in motion, a fact we readily accept today.

There is an interesting and perhaps humorous point to mention here, one that applies to many other science-related verses in the Quran. In chapter 2, I described how the prophet Muhammad initially faced stiff resistance to his message. Part of this resistance by many tribal leaders and wealthy individuals was in the form of a negative propaganda campaign against the new prophet's character and state of mind. This smear campaign was not only intended for the ears of the Meccans but was also done to dissuade anyone living in nearby towns and cities from seriously considering the message Muhammad brought forth. So, the tribal "media machine" began attacking Muhammad's sanity and credibility by calling him "crazy" because he spoke of verses that made no apparent sense whatsoever.

I have often wondered whether verse 27:88 was one of these verses. After all, if any one of us was asked to tell a group of primitive sixth-century desert people that, contrary to what they see with their very own eyes, mountains are not fixed but are instead in constant motion, what would their response be? Yet, mountains move as Earth moves in its orbit around its axis, as well around the sun.

Limited Lifetime of Our Sun

It's well accepted by scientists today that every star in the universe is "born," lives its "life," and eventually "dies." Our sun, being just another star, also follows this same progression. The sun was born about 5 billion years ago

---

62. *Heliocentricity* (the idea that Earth revolves around the sun) was proposed prior to Copernicus and Galileo, but these scientists (along with Kepler) confirmed its truth through a fully predictive mathematical model.

and will continue to shine through about the next 5 billion years in what scientists believe to be a 10-billion-year lifespan.

Stars eventually die because they exhaust their fuel. This fuel drives nuclear reactions constantly taking place inside of stars, similar to how gasoline powers a car engine. Through these nuclear reactions, atoms of certain chemical elements fuse (join) together in nuclear fusion processes that result in the creation of different (and heavier) chemical elements while releasing large amounts of energy in the forms of outward pressure, light, and heat. And just as humans go through individual stages of life, stars too, experience their own individual life stages. Stars' life stages vary from one star to another based upon each star's individual characteristics, with the initial mass of the star being the most important.[63] In the case of our sun, for instance, its luminosity gradually increased with time, as it was about 30 percent less luminous at the moment of its birth than it is today. In a few billion years, as it approaches the end of its life, the sun will gradually grow much larger in size and become what's known as a red giant, where it will grow so large that it may even engulf Earth. Following the red giant phase, the sun will begin to shrink in size and become what's known as a white dwarf, where it will be no larger than the size of Earth (the sun will not shine or generate heat at that point since all nuclear reactions would have ceased by then). The Quran pointed to our sun's limited lifetime in the following verse:

> And the sun runs to a stable state [or end, finish] for her. That is the estimation of the one filled with overpowering strength and knowledge.
>
> (36:38)

Let's examine some of the key words used by this verse. The first is *runs* (*tejri*: "runs, races, flows"). Clearly, this word implies a journey of some sort. Next, let's examine the word for *a stable state* (*musta'qir*: "stable, settled, steady, constant, quiet"). This word implies that the sun will end its journey at this stable or unchanging "thing," which I propose to be a set future state. It's rather curious how the verse does not specify where this stable end is or, in other words, why the Quran did not associate any spatial attributes with this stable end. Almost everyone reading this verse would find it perfectly reasonable to assume that what the Quran means is running toward or within a stable "location." However, by omitting this association and

---

63. The mass of an object is a measure of how much matter is inside that object.

referring to a journey, the verse leaves open the possibility that this stable end may not be a physical location, but a stable end "in time."[64]

Next, let's examine the words *for her* (*le'ha*: "for her, hers"). The verse seems to imply that the *estimation* mentioned in the second part of the verse is one that's specific to our sun. This agrees with our scientific understanding of the individual lives of stars as just noted, since the life of any star is mostly dictated by its mass. The more massive the star, the quicker it burns through its fuel and the shorter it lives. For instance, a star that's a number of times more massive than our sun may only live for a small fraction of the 10-billion-year lifetime our sun will live. The Quran could have easily deleted *for her* and kept the verse more concise, but again, these words, although appearing extraneous, hold a more insightful meaning.

The next important key word to ponder is *estimation* (*tuq'deer*: "estimation, assessment, evaluation"). Scientists believe that our particular sun played a vitally important role with respect to the existence and evolution of most (if not all) life on planet Earth. Life, especially complex life, took an extraordinarily lengthy amount of time to evolve on our planet. For example, it took animals more than 3 billion years after life started on Earth to appear on the scene. Had our sun been more massive, it might have died out long before animal life could have had the chance to evolve to the degree of complexity to which it did. Therefore, *estimation*, in the context just described, also holds an important and insightful meaning.

The next set of key words is how the god chose to describe his being as having *overpowering strength and knowledge* (*azeez*: "strong, powerful;" *aleem*: "expert, knowing"). Within the Quran, it's generally true that different godly attributes are used in different verse contexts, depending upon the general meaning or message of the verse. Thus, the choice of description(s) used for the god by any particular verse needs to be carefully studied, as is the case here with the use of the attributes of overpowering strength and knowledge.

As noted earlier, the sun is a tremendous fireball constantly undergoing nuclear reactions to generate the enormous levels of energy it generates during every second of its 10-billion-year lifespan.[65] These are the same kind of nuclear reactions used by atomic bombs, the destructive power of which we've all heard about. To further appreciate the sheer power of the sun, think of how we normally seek shelter and shade from the sun's heat on a hot summer day, even though it's quite far away. In fact, the sun is

---

64. Verses 13:2, 31:29, 35:13, and 39:5 support the understanding that this journey is one through time.

65. The sun generates more than 3 million times the annual energy consumption of the United States *every second*.

so far away that, despite going around Earth's equator seven times in one second, it takes light an entire eight minutes to reach us from it.[66]

So with this appreciation for the sun's power, the verse's choice of *over-powering strength* is aptly appropriate. Why did the verse use *knowledge*? This is most likely related to the estimation of the sun's lifetime as we previously discussed, in that knowledge (of what's to follow) must precede the act of estimation.

In addition to the verse we're discussing here, the Quran has pointed to the limited lives of stars in general through the following verse:

> *And when the stars are darkened [or fade away].*
> (81:2)

The key word here is *darkened* (*in'ked'eret*: "to fade, lose luster, become dull"[67]). We can interpret this darkening of stars as stars consuming all their fuel, thereby ending their ability to sustain the nuclear reactions needed to produce the light energy generated during their normal lives.

Black Holes

Black holes are perhaps the greatest and most mysterious objects in the universe today. When a massive star, usually many times bigger than our sun, runs out of fuel, it can no longer generate the outward pressure required to support its heavy weight (this outward force opposes the inward force of gravity). When this happens, the star begins to collapse onto itself. There are different levels of collapse, though, based upon how massive the star was when the collapse started. The actual events that take place, which are part of what's referred to as a supernova explosion, are truly astounding.

We live in a world where atoms consist of smaller protons and electrons that, under normal everyday circumstances, keep their distance from each other. The electrons circle the protons, which are located inside the nucleus of the atom, from relatively far away (recall the stadium example), and this

---

66. Speaking of things reaching us from the sun, hundreds of billions of particles called "neutrinos" strike and penetrate our bodies every second of every day of our lives, even during the night, when the sun is on the other side of Earth. No need to lose any sleep over this though; neutrinos, which are produced every time a proton turns into a neutron during the sun's fusion process, are totally harmless and will continue to travel completely unhindered through the vast expanses of space for a very long time (they do so because the only force they recognize is the weak nuclear force, which only works at extremely small distances).

67. In some instances, my translation of a word may not match *Al-Mawrid*'s because I use the context of the verse when translating. In this case, because stars are shiny (i.e., light-emitting) objects, I translate *in'ked'eret* as a darkening.

separation is very important to the stability of the chemical elements that make up our existence. Well, this normal state of affairs no longer holds true during the collapse of a massive star. During such a collapse, electrons are brought closer and closer until they literally fuse with the protons to form new constituents called neutrons, and a neutron star is born.[68]

This neutron star is a mind-bogglingly massive object that packs in an immense amount of matter. To appreciate this, let's imagine two of our suns (1 million Earths can fit inside the sun) shrunk down in size and packed into a tiny space equal to that of the island of Manhattan.[69] Because of the resulting matter density, a scientist once claimed that a teaspoon of neutron star material weighs as much as Earth's Mount Everest. Another scientist further claimed that if a mushroom were dropped on the surface of a neutron star, an explosion would result that would release as much energy as an atomic bomb! Again, all this is because of just how much matter is packed in even a tiny volume of space inside a neutron star.

The next phase in the collapse after the neutron star, if the star is massive enough (about fifteen times the mass of our sun), is what's known as a black hole. The collapse in this case is so immense that absolutely nothing can stop it. The matter of the original star literally collapses into what scientists call a "singularity," a vanishingly small point characterized by "infinities." These infinities include infinite density (because the matter is squeezed into an infinitely small amount of space) and infinite space-time curvature.[70] This singularity is significant because it is at this imaginary point where the known laws of physics begin to break down, and no one knows what actually takes place inside the singularity or what may lie (if anything) beyond it.

Black holes possess another interesting quality. Because black holes are characterized by infinite density, they exert a tremendous gravitational pull on nearby objects. These objects are literally sucked into the black hole if they happen to be close enough (within what's known as the event horizon). Beyond this, the pull is so strong that not even the fastest thing in the universe—light—can escape, which is why this kind of hole is called "black," since no light can ever reach us from it. In a sense, if we were to look up into space to see a black hole—if someone told us that one was

---

68. If the star is less than 1.4 times the mass of our sun, a white dwarf is born, in which case the electrons are not yet fused with the protons, but the result is still a very dense object.

69. In the case of a white dwarf, the original sun-sized star is shrunk to the size of Earth.

70. Space-time is a construct proposed by Einstein, which combines the three known dimensions of space with that of time into a new, four-dimensional space-time "fabric."

there, for instance—we'll see nothing, even if a supermassive black hole was right there.[71] With this baffling discussion fresh in mind, let's now examine the following verses:

> By the sky and the loud one. And how will you [Muhammad] know [or sense] what the loud one is? The star that punctures [or the puncturing star].
>
> (86:1–3)

The first important word we want to examine in this verse is *by* (from the Arabic letter *weh*: "by," used for swearing oaths). This word is normally used to signify a pledge and to refer to something held in deep regard. This pledging is, in my view, one of the most beautiful aspects of the Quran (or, more appropriately, of the god). This god swears by the holiness of creation, and the god's love and reverence for it (as we normally swear to something we hold dear). Taking such an oath is a recurring theme in the Quran and has been associated with things that we humans would perhaps consider to be insignificant.

The verses then introduce *the loud one* (*tariq*: "hammerer, striker, knocker, beater"[72]) and state that it is something that Muhammad cannot know or see (from *ed'rek*: "to perceive, to see, to be made aware of"). In addition, the verses again use *sky* (*sema'a*), so that this loud one is something "of the sky." The meaning of the loud one is further clarified in that it is an actual star (*neh'jim*) and not just any star but a star that *punctures* something (*tha'qib*: "penetrating, piercing, puncturing").

Given this particular set of words, along with the verses' general meaning, I have come to believe that what these verses are referring to is the black-hole-creation event we just learned about.

Some of us may be thinking that the puncturing referenced in the verses is the puncturing of the space-time fabric as noted earlier, but this may not be scientifically correct. Scientists simply do not know what happens to space-time at the singularity, and I would be stretching scientific truth by stating that space-time becomes punctured during such a black-hole-creation event. However, I find it curious that the Quran chose a word for *loud* that is also normally associated with the night (as in *black*), and I find it equally curious that *punctures* implies a *hole* being created, since something does not become punctured unless a hole is also created in the process.

---

71. A supermassive black hole is a black hole with hundreds of thousands to billions of suns inside.

72. *Tariq* has also been used to denote someone appearing "at night."

In addition to these verses, the Quran provides yet more verses that possibly point to the existence of what we've come to know as black holes:

> *And I [the god] swear by the fallings of the stars, and this is surely a great pledge, if you [humanity] only knew: that this Quran is surely enlightening.*
>
> (56:75–77)

> *And I [the god] swear by the ones that recede. The moving hidden ones. And by the night as it approaches, and by the morning's first light: that this [the Quran] is surely the speech of a noble [or gracious] envoy [referring to the angel Gabriel communicating the Quran to the prophet Muhammad].*
>
> (81:15–19)

> *By the falling [or collapsing] star: your [humanity's] friend [referring to Muhammad] has not veered from the truth, nor is he misguided. Nor does he speak his fancies [or desires]. He is but inspired through revelation. Taught by the one with immense power [referring to Gabriel and also described in other verses as an angel of substantial might].*
>
> (53:1–5)

In the first set of verses, the god swears by stars *falling* (*mewaqi'i:* "falling, tumbling, dropping") and talks about how these events are of great significance.[73] In the second set of verses, the word for *the ones that recede* (*khun'nes:* "stars in general or a class of planets that experience a retrograde orbit"[74]) refers to celestial objects in general or to planets that are receding and hidden from view. The second set also makes mention of *moving hidden ones* (*jawar:* "fast movers;" *kun'ness:* "planets hidden from sight by being too close to the sun and obstructed by her rays"[75]), immediately following mention of *the ones that recede*. This expression, with its "things in hiding" connotation, alludes to an action that resembles that of a "feeding" black hole. You can think of the black hole "hiding" celestial objects, thus causing them to become invisible.[76] Black holes have also been discovered to

---

73. Some have translated *mewaqi'i* as "positions." However, the Arabic word for "position" comes from the root word *fall* and literally translates to "where something falls."

74. Penrice, *Dictionary and Glossary*, 68.

75. Penrice, *Dictionary and Glossary*, 197.

76. Astronomers have recently observed a black hole that devours the mass equivalent of two Earths an hour.

move through space, so *moving* in the verses accurately applies to the actual behavior of black holes. I also find it interesting that verses 81:15–19 use the word *night* (*layl*) immediately following *moving hidden ones*. The last set of verses may even be talking about a supernova event (the star collapse described earlier in the section), since they use the words *star* (*neh'jim*) and *falling* or *collapsing* (*hawa*: "to fall down, drop, tumble, sink").[77] Of interest to note in the last set, too, is the mention of the angel Gabriel along with his *immense power* (*shadeed el-quwa*: "very strong, forceful"), also quite fitting within the context of a supernova explosion.

The Asteroid Belt

The asteroid belt (also known as the main asteroid belt) occupies a region in our solar system between the planets Mars and Jupiter and contains millions of rocky bodies of various shapes, called asteroids. These asteroids, which can be as small as a dust particle or as large as a dwarf planet, are believed to have almost formed a planet if Jupiter's immense gravitational pull hadn't prevented such a formation. Scientists estimate that there are about 1 million asteroids that are more than 3000 feet (1 km) across in the asteroid belt, with the largest, Ceres, measuring more than 600 miles (1000 km) across. In spite of their sheer number, though, the combined mass of the asteroids in the asteroid belt makes up no more than 5 percent of our moon's mass, which itself is no more than 2 percent of Earth's mass. Many of us have probably seen various artists' depictions of the asteroid belt in science magazines or on TV, illustrating these asteroids lined up in close proximity to each other. However, these depictions are not entirely realistic, as the asteroids are spaced fairly far apart.

In addition to the asteroid belt, our solar system contains two more body-rich regions. The first is the Kuiper belt, named after the Dutch-American astronomer Gerard Kuiper and located outside of the orbit of the planet Neptune. The Kuiper belt contains numerous comets, with the most famous being Halley's comet, which visits our planet once every seventy-six years. The second region, home to *trillions* of comets, is the Oort cloud, named after the Dutch astronomer Jan Oort. This region of space is so far away that it takes light almost an entire year to reach it from our sun. The asteroid belt is special among other regions, however, because the majority of the bodies that can cross Earth's orbit and impact our planet, with quite devastating consequences at times, originate from the asteroid belt.

I believe that the Quran has made mention of these asteroid- and comet-rich regions of space in the following verse:

---

77. *Neh'jim* specifically translates into "star," not "meteor." The Quran uses the word *Shihab* when describing a meteor.

> *Do they not extend their sights to the fliers above them forming*
> *a line and [or while] they jerk. No one can hold them except*
> *the one filled with mercy. Surely, he [the god] is observant of all*
> *things.*

(67:19)

This verse has traditionally been difficult to interpret, as evident from the verse's general lack of clarity. In my view, though, the verse provides a clear and direct reference to an asteroid belt or something similar, as just described. Let's take a closer look at the key words and attempt to gain further insight. First, we can reasonably deduce that the verse is describing something quite distant, as the phrase *extend their sights* (from *ya'row*: "see, behold," and *ila*: "to, toward, until, up to, as far as") is used instead of just "see." How can sight be extended? The answer is through a special light-magnifying instrument, such as a telescope, microscope, or binoculars (things not even known in the sixth century). However, the verse was specific in that this extension must go above, and therefore this extension of sight must be through something like an astronomical telescope.

The next important word is *flier* (*tayr*). *Flier* usually signifies anything that can fly and typically means "bird" in today's use of the Arabic word. But interpreting this verse as pertaining to birds makes little sense, as the verse started out asking that we "extend our sights" as opposed to asking us to just see. These particular *fliers* are also described as forming a *line* (*sa'fat*: "lined up, aligned") and experiencing some sort of *jerk* (from *yek'bith*: "being held, gripped, grasped").[78] In addition, the verse states that these *fliers* need to be somehow held (*yumsik*: "hold, grab, grip, seize"), and *mercy* (*rah'meh*: "mercy, kindness") was used in conjunction with this holding.

Of course, the one filled with mercy is the god and, as I noted in a previous section, the Quran sometimes uses other godly attributes in lieu of saying "the god," based upon the specific context and meaning of a verse. In this particular verse, the use of *the one filled with mercy* when referring to this holding is quite appropriate, if we interpret these fliers as being bodies of an asteroid or comet belt.

As noted earlier, most of the asteroids that can impact Earth originate from the asteroid belt. Some of these impacts are also quite catastrophic, as scientists believe happened about 65 million years ago, when an asteroid the size of Mount Everest struck Earth near the present-day Yucatan peninsula, wiping out all the dinosaurs along with about 65 percent of all

---

78. I use the term *jerk* because the verse says that an action of gripping is required, thus also implying the desire to escape. The combination of these two factors can be thought of as a jerk.

other living species. Scientists also believe that the asteroids in the asteroid belt are under constant influences from neighboring asteroids, as well as from other planets, most notably nearby Jupiter, with its immense gravitational pull. The actual term used by scientists to refer to these gravitational influences (or perturbations) is *dynamic excitation* (a term that itself can perhaps be crudely approximated as a jerk).

It is thus possible for the forces affecting any one asteroid to push that asteroid out of its place and into space toward the inner planets of the solar system (Mercury, Venus, Earth, and Mars). If the asteroid comes close to Earth and if Earth's gravitational pull is strong enough to capture the ejected asteroid, potentially dire consequences can result if the asteroid is large enough, as was the case 65 million years ago. And so we can see why the special attribute of *the one filled with mercy* was used by the verse when describing the holding of these fliers as they experience their jerking motion.[79]

Formation of the Chemical Elements in Stars

As was initially described in chapter 3, we know today that everything that is normal matter in the universe is made up of one or more chemical elements. These elements include well-known ones such as hydrogen (the most abundant element in the universe), oxygen (a gas we breathe to help produce our energy), carbon (also known as "the element of life"), and calcium (a nutrient needed for proper bone health), as well as some other elements many of us have probably never heard of, such as osmium, californium, and ytterbium. In total, there are about one hundred distinct elements in existence, which also vary in their degree of abundance and how each came to be.

Hydrogen, for example, was created shortly after the big bang. Helium, the next element in the periodic table, was also created during this stage, as was the element lithium. Beyond these three elements, however, the creation of more chemical elements took on a different path. Elements beyond lithium required the formation of "first generation" stars. These were the first stars to form some 200 million years after the big bang from hydrogen, helium, and lithium (but mostly from hydrogen). These stars also functioned as "factories" for manufacturing even more chemical elements through the nuclear reactions described earlier in this chapter. Beyond the first generation stars, newer generations of follow-on stars—themselves now made of some of the chemical elements manufactured by first generation stars—were born and in turn became factories for making even heavier

---

79. Scientists estimate that there are a million asteroids in the vicinity of Earth, each capable of laying waste to an entire metropolitan area.

elements during similar nucleosynthesis processes.[80] The stories behind the creation of some of these chemical elements are quite fascinating, with the story of how carbon, the life-enabling element, was created being a good case in point (and one I encourage you to learn more about[81]).

More, and even heavier, elements were also created when massive stars came to the end of their lives, collapsed, and violently exploded to create the heaviest elements (the same supernova explosions mentioned in the Black Holes section). Thus, the chemical elements we know today came to be after the formation and death of several generations of stars. Many of these elements were further used to "make life" on planet Earth, including the stuff you and I are made of (of the hundred or so chemical elements, about two dozen have proven to be vital for life). With this short background on a fascinating topic, let's now examine the following verses:

> And he [the god] put to your [humanity's] use [or benefit] the night and the day, and the sun and the moon, and the stars are made to benefit you through his will [or command]. Surely, in all of this are clear signs [or matters to contemplate and reflect upon] for mindful [or intelligent, thoughtful] people. And what he created [or made, sowed] for you in Earth [or the land] of varying colors. Surely, in all of this is a sign for those who reflect. And he is the one who put the sea to your use, so you eat from it soft flesh and you extract jewelry you wear, and you [Muhammad] see the ships through the waves, and so that you [humanity] seek benefits, hoping you are thankful. And he set on the earth [or land] anchors, so that she does not sway with them, and rivers, and pathways, hoping you find your ways. And guideposts, **and through the stars they find their ways**.
>
> (16:12–16)

These verses are rather clear in their general meaning, but let's carefully study them, beginning with *and the stars are made to benefit you through his will [or command]*. The key words in this expression are *made to benefit* (*musa'kharat*: "exploited, utilized, employed, used") and *will* (*um'r*: "order, command, instruction, directive"). Prior to this expression, the verses had just spoken of the moon and the sun and their associated benefits. What are these benefits? We know that the moon provides us with the benefits of nocturnal light, a visible way to mark the passing of time, and the ocean

---

80. Iron, the twenty-sixth element in the periodic table of elements, is the heaviest element that can be made by stars in this fashion.

81. See Roston, *The Carbon Age*, 18.

tides. The moon has also benefitted us in less obvious ways. For instance, the moon played a crucial role in slowing Earth's rotation around its axis early in our planet's life, and it helps keep Earth's axial tilt stable (this tilt is responsible for our four seasons). This tilt stability is especially important in preserving a long-term stable climate for Earth and for the life she hosts.[82] In terms of benefits from the sun, we know that the sun provides us with the benefits of light, heat, time, and other life-enabling benefits (we simply would not be here without our sun).

But what benefits do the stars provide? We can perhaps state that their most obvious benefit is their facility in providing guidance at night, as ships have navigated by the stars for thousands of years. Is that it? Or is there some bigger benefit stars provide? To make the case that something more interesting is being said in these verses, I'll need to provide some further linguistic insight.

First, the Quran could have structured the verses' first part more concisely as *And he put to your use the night and the day, and the sun and the moon and the stars*, thereby eliminating *are made to benefit you through his will [or command]*. That would have been a more economical way of expressing the same meaning, especially if stars were meant to only provide the single benefit of guidance. It's thus possible, then, that the verses are placing special emphasis on these stars by associating *are made to benefit you* with them. The next clue comes from the use of *through his will [or command]*. We can certainly postulate that the "will (or 'command, directive') of the god" is important in realizing anything and everything in existence. However, this *will* was specifically called out for the stars and not the sun, moon, day, or night. Something special is thus going on with respect to these stars that requires "the will of the god" to be explicitly called out for these stars and not for any of the other mentioned benefits. The third clue comes from the verses' use of the word *mindful* (*ya'qiloon*: "mindful, intelligent, brainy") in association with the first set of benefits, while the next set uses the attribute *reflective* (*ya'thekeroon* from *thikr*: "remembrance, reminiscence"). This implies that something that requires mindfulness, intelligence, and keen thought is associated with the first set of benefits, urging the reader of the Quran to further explore these first set of benefits. Finally, and most importantly, the verses had already clearly and explicitly stated that these stars were meant to benefit us through guidance (the bolded text in the verses).

Therefore, if the first mention of the benefits of the stars was to only provide guidance, then the Quran can be perceived as being somewhat

---

82. We'll also see in the next chapter how some scientists believe that complex life itself would not have arisen on Earth in the absence of a relatively large moon.

redundant in this respect. The Quran, however, is *not* a redundant book. I have come to accept this based on years of study and research into the Quran (if anything, I think the Quran is probably not verbose enough).[83] So, if we can entertain the possibility that the Quran is not a needlessly redundant book, then the first mention of star benefits reflects something that goes beyond the stars providing mere guidance.

When I first began to study these verses and started to contemplate the points I just mentioned, I became more and more convinced that the verses were at least in part referring to the formation of chemical elements by the stars. I was 90 percent confident that such an interpretation was correct. However, that confidence changed to 100 percent when I noted the word *colors* (*elwan*) later in the verses. This word turns out to be a revealing clue.

During my research into the Quran, there were times during which I would contemplate a particular verse meaning, and this meaning would be immediately confirmed in the next verse or set of verses through a particular word or phrase that affirmed what I was thinking about, and the verses' use of *colors* here illustrates this. The verses do not need to specifically use *colors* to denote a variety of things that spring from the earth.[84] As a matter of fact, *colors* is quite a poor choice to describe such a variety. We all know that plants are mostly green in color, so the use of *colors* to denote plant variety does not make much sense in my view. Instead of *colors*, the Quran could have used *shapes* or *tastes* to serve as a better description for such variety. After all, every plant has a unique shape and possesses a unique taste. On the other hand, plants do not have unique colors, at least not to the degree to which shapes and tastes are unique. Thus, *colors* is perhaps significant in some other sense.[85]

It turns out that color is a fundamental property that identifies a particular chemical element. When a chemical element radiates, absorbs, or

---

83. This is not to say that there are no repeated verses in the Quran. This, however, is being repetitive, not redundant, since redundancy carries a negative and needlessly wasteful connotation. A rather simple analogy is if I remind my spouse to drop an extremely important letter in the mail. In such a case, I am being repetitive, not redundant.

84. The Arabic word for *created* (*ther'a*: "to create, multiply, increase") is traditionally associated within the context of farming and agriculture.

85. The Quran uses *colors* to describe plant variety in two other verses. In verse 35:27, the Quran uses *colors* to describe the great variety of fruits that come from the earth. The Quran also uses *colors* in verse 39:21 but does so only as a contrast to the color yellow (i.e., the Quran asks the reader to observe the variety of plant colors and how all these colors eventually turn into yellow–implying that all things come to an end regardless of how beautiful they may be at the beginning). In this case, too, the use of *colors* is a logical choice.

reflects light, it does so through a special color (or band of colors) that is related to the atomic makeup of that particular element (as you probably learned in school, the color you see for something is the color of light that's reflected by that object into your eyes). So the element oxygen, for instance, emits a green light when it becomes excited or energized, while the element nitrogen (specifically ionized nitrogen) emits a blue light during such excitation.[86] In fact, the science that's concerned with the study of light colors from various objects is called *spectroscopy*. Spectroscopy is based upon the close relationship between color and chemical composition and has been used by astronomers to determine the chemical makeup (and associated characteristics) of distant stars and other celestial objects within our universe. A prime example of this has been the discovery of the chemical element helium, which also derives its name from the source of its discovery, the sun. In 1868, the French astronomer Pierre Janssen discovered this element after analyzing light coming from our sun during a solar eclipse, and thus helium was known to exist prior to its discovery on Earth.

The relationship between color and chemical makeup is well understood through the rules of quantum mechanics, the special branch of physics initially mentioned in chapter 3. As stated earlier, the Pauli exclusion principle is the rule by which chemical elements take on their individual atomic structures (and chemical properties). It's this precise atomic structure that determines the exact frequency (or wavelength) at which light is emitted, absorbed, or reflected by a particular chemical element, or, in other words, how an element's color is defined (color and frequency are directly related in that the color of light is dictated by the precise frequency of light that is being emitted, absorbed, or reflected). Thus, the Quran's use of *colors*, while appearing inconsequential on the surface, actually communicates an insightful aspect of how we, along with almost everything else in the universe, came to be through the birth and death of many generations of countless numbers of stars.

The Big Bang

As was previously stated, the big bang signifies what scientists believe to be the creation event of our universe some 13.7 billion years ago. No one is certain of what took place exactly at, or just before, the instant of the big bang, but scientists have been able to reconstruct a fairly accurate picture of how the universe unfolded and evolved in the seconds, minutes, and years since then up to our present day. It's rather astounding how, through

---

86. The same element can emit more than one color, depending upon the degree to which it becomes excited or energized.

observation, thoughtfulness, and experimentation, scientists have been able to reveal precise details of events that took place in the far-distant past, long before our planet was even created.[87]

A trifecta of an extremely high density of energy, extremely high temperatures, and extremely high pressures characterized the period just after the big bang. This period was also characterized by very rapid spatial expansion of the universe during an epoch called *inflation*. During inflation, the universe expanded exponentially by an unimaginably humungous factor and in a very brief period of time.[88] As inflation ended, the most fundamental constituents of matter, called elementary particles and which included quarks and leptons, began to appear. The universe was in such an excited state then that particle-antiparticle pairs were being continuously created and annihilated during powerful collisions (an antiparticle can be thought of as the opposite of a particle, just like we can think of the color black as being the opposite of white). At some point during this state, an as-yet-unknown mechanism allowed for the existence of more particles than antiparticles, which in turn led to the creation of more matter than antimatter. It's believed that for every billion units of antimatter, there existed 1 billion and one units of matter, and this tiny difference was absolutely necessary for the follow-on creation of everything that is matter in the universe, including galaxies, stars, planets, and, of course, us!

As the universe continued to expand and cool, and as the energy of these elementary particles began to drop as a result of this expansion and cooling, something called *symmetry breaking* took place. Symmetry breaking was responsible for the creation of our present four fundamental forces as well as the present parameters of elementary particles. At about one-millionth of a second (yes, everything I just described took place well before this millionth-of-a-second mark), quarks and gluons (also known as force particles) combined to form protons and neutrons, the particles that typically constitute the nucleus of the atom. The protons and neutrons did not combine, however, until a few minutes after the big bang, and most protons remained in an independent state in the form of hydrogen nuclei.

Fast forward to 379,000 years after the big bang, and the electrons (which are a type of lepton) are now combined with atomic nuclei to form the first chemical elements of hydrogen and helium, which, as we learned, were

---

87. The question of *why* (or why should) we have been able to unravel so much of the universe's inner secrets is one of the most profound questions being asked by scientists today.

88. To get a glimpse of what this expansion was like, imagine an ant becoming much larger than our Milky Way galaxy, with its 200 billion suns, in much shorter than the blink of an eye!

used for making the first-generation stars.[89] These first-generation stars were born after hydrogen and helium were available in significant enough quantities to form massive clouds of gas and dust, also known as stellar nurseries, from which a great multitude of stars were born.[90] Let's now examine the following verses that I believe summarize this creation event:

> *Are you [humanity] more difficult to create or was the sky?*
> *[The god] built her. [He, the god] lifted [or elevated, raised]*
> *her ceiling so made her [the sky] uniform [or equal]. [The god]*
> *darkened her night and extracted her sunrise. And Earth after*
> *that [the god] rolled.*
>
> (79:27–30)

These verses have never been correctly interpreted, because *sky* (*sema'a*) was interpreted to be our Earth's sky. However, Earth's sky (our atmosphere) only came about after Earth itself was created, as we'll discuss in greater detail in the next chapter, so interpreting *sky* as Earth's atmosphere would result in a major conflict with established science. Clearly, the verses at hand are describing events that took place prior to the formation of Earth itself, so *sky* should be understood here to refer to the universe.[91] Before continuing with the explanation for these verses, though, I'll need to provide a little more detail of the events that took place following the big bang.

According to the big bang theory, the entire universe was squeezed into a size smaller than that of an atom and was thus in state of tremendous density and temperature. During the epoch of inflation, however, the universe, in addition to expanding by a tremendous amount, experienced a "smoothing" of its matter, and such matter became uniformly distributed throughout the universe. Today we know that our universe is surprisingly uniform in terms of the general distribution of matter on a cosmic scale and that uniformity has been observed to be better than one part in a hundred

---

89. We can now begin to appreciate how immensely hot and energetic the very early universe really was, given that it took several hundred thousand years for things to begin to settle down so that the most elementary chemical elements could begin to form.

90. To see what these stellar nurseries might have looked like, search the Internet for "the pillars of creation," and look at the impressive picture taken by the Hubble space telescope of a star-producing region of space.

91. Some past interpreters have translated the Arabic word for *rolled* as "flattened," while others translated it as "made into the shape of an ostrich egg." However, one of the earliest uses of the word was to denote a spherical or disk-like object used by the children of Mecca during the time of the prophet (El-Shirbini, *El-Ijaz*, 95).

thousand.[92] Thus, when the verses talk about *making her [the sky] uniform [or equal]* (*sow'wa*: "equalize, smoothen, level off, make even"), I believe they are referring to this equalization of matter in the universe. With respect to *darkened her night and extracted her sunrise*, there are a number of key words I need to provide translations for. These are *darkened* (*ugh'tasha*: "to become dark"), *night* (*layl*), *extracted* (*akh'raja*: "take out, bring out"), and *sunrise* (*thuha*: "morning").

I mentioned how the early universe was essentially made up of various elementary particles. These particles constituted a sort of milky (or opaque) cloud that lasted up until 379,000 years after the big bang—the point when the first chemical elements formed. The cloud was opaque because photons, the known particles of light, could only travel very short distances before they met and were scattered by free-roaming particles. However, after 379,000 years, free electrons became much less energetic (as the temperature of the universe dropped) and so they combined with atomic nuclei to form the first chemical elements. The combination of electrons with nuclei resulted in something that was quite significant, however, in that it allowed the photons to travel through the universe unhindered, thus allowing the universe to become "transparent." "First light" had shone, as light particles were able to travel freely throughout, which they have continued to do to our present day. This is what I believe the verses are referring to when stating that sunrise (or morning) was extracted. Also, there are two words in *lifted her ceiling* that need to be further clarified. These are *lifted* (*rafa'a*: "raised, elevated, increased, jacked up") and *ceiling* (*semk*: "roof, ceiling"). Therefore, *lifting her ceiling* most likely refers to the inflation epoch, when the universe expanded while being in a state of tremendously high density (we can probably imagine this expansion as a "lifting" or "elevation" of a ceiling, as noted in the verses).

It's important to note something quite intriguing here about the laws of physics and how they sometimes go against their normal rules when certain conditions are present. When the big bang occurred, the most significant force present was that of gravity. However, because gravity is an attractive force, you might have expected the universe to collapse on itself immediately following the big bang. This obviously did not happen; instead, the universe expanded and inflated as was described earlier. It turns out that gravity was actually _repulsive_ immediately following the big bang. This reversal of behavior for such a fundamental force was the engine that drove the follow-on expansion of the universe and enabled the universe

---

92. This high degree of uniformity is roughly analogous to us, our children, our grandchildren, our great-grandchildren, and six or seven more generations after that (274 years total) eating the exact same breakfast every morning.

to become what it is today. So, when the Quran mentions *lifting her ceiling*, it's referring to something quite important and out of the ordinary. This realization that the Quran focuses on particularly wondrous phenomena is an experience I had with many other verses cited in this book.

The Big Crunch?

Now you may be wondering: If the universe began with the big bang and has been expanding ever since, how will it end? Will the expansion slow, stop, and reverse? Or will the universe continue to expand forever?

This intriguing question lacks a definite answer based upon our scientific knowledge today. Theories that attempt to describe the fate of the universe include the big freeze, the big rip, and the big crunch, among others. However, the most favored theory today calls for the universe to continue on its current expansion course and to do so forever (forever should be qualified here, as there are several theories that also describe what may happen to the universe in that distant future). Like I said, though, scientists need more observations and a better understanding of the structure and components of the cosmos before they can provide more concrete answers.

The Quran has also weighed in on this topic through a few verses that possibly point to the big crunch scenario as the ultimate fate of our universe. In verse 86:11, the Quran describes the *sky* (again, *sema'a*) as one that "returns" (*rejee*: "return, revert, go back"), while in verse 21:104, the Quran describes how the *sky* will eventually become "folded onto itself" (*tawee*: "rolling up, folding, tucking") and will "return"; it uses a *scroll* (*sij'jil*) being rolled onto itself as an example. In this particular analogy, the Quran also seems to indicate that our universe—assuming we can interpret *sky* as the universe here—is a "flat" one. This flatness is yet another aspect of the cosmos still under debate, with the other two topology choices being positively curved (like the surface of a spherical ball) and negatively curved (like the surface of a saddle).

Will Our Sun Engulf the Moon?

Earlier I described how scientists believe that in about 5 billion years the sun will become much larger in size and turn into what's known as a red giant. I also mentioned how scientists are currently unsure of whether or not the sun will grow large enough to engulf Earth (scientists seem to agree that the sun will engulf the two innermost planets, Mercury and Venus). However, according to a couple of verses in the Quran, the sun will not grow large enough to engulf our moon. In verse 75:9, the Quran talks of the "coming together" (*jem'i*: "gather, collect, join, combine") of the sun and the moon, while in another verse (verse 36:40, previewed in the Stellar and Planetary Orbits section), the Quran states *it is not appropriate for the sun to reach the moon.* This second verse is usually interpreted as the sun maintaining spatial separation from the moon, but the choice of word for *reach* (from *id'rak*: "catch up with, overtake, reach") is one that implies a grasping or reaching out action. Together with the first verse, which alludes to the sun and moon eventually approaching each other, we can perhaps conclude that the sun will not grow large enough to engulf our moon when it becomes a red giant. Whether the sun engulfs Earth or not, it's probably safe to assume that none of our species will be around then to witness such a horrific event.

Do We Live in a World beyond Three Dimensions?

This is an interesting question indeed. According to string theory, our universe may contain up to ten spatial dimensions, with the seven additional dimensions being very small and completely outside the realm of our everyday experience. Of course, no one has confirmed this experimentally, so the jury is still out, so to speak.

Within the Quran, however, there are verses that seem to point to the possibility of the existence of more dimensions beyond those we are used to living in. The first of these verses was provided within the Quran Sample Chapter section of chapter 1. We saw then that the Quran talks of the *two easts* (*mesh'riqain*) and the *two wests* (*megh'ribain*) and it does so immediately following mention of the creation of man and of creatures referred to by the Quran as *jinn*. For quite a while, I didn't understand what the Quran meant by *two easts* or *two wests*, nor was I able to find a good explanation about it. After all, there is only one east and only one west from any point on Earth. It then dawned on me that perhaps what the Quran is communicating here is that one of these *easts* belongs in the world of humans, while the other *east* belongs in the world of jinn. And if we interpret an *east* or a *west* as a "dimension," then perhaps the Quran is stating that we and the jinn live in separate dimensions, even though we may be sharing the same space.[93] In yet another instance (verse 70:40), the Quran expands this description of *east* and *west* beyond the two and talks about the god being the life giver of *all easts* (*meshariq*) and *all wests* (*megharib*), which again implies there could potentially be many other worlds, with each world occupying a separate set of dimensions out there. This possibility is further confirmed by yet another verse in the Quran:

---

93. A good analogy to this is when you're riding a boat on the surface of a body of water, when the water's depth can be thought of as a new, unseen dimension by those on the water's surface.

And we [the god] surely created above you [humanity] seven ways [or paths, roads] and we were never unaware of the creation.

(23:17)

This verse is quite curious because it talks about the number seven, which we'll discover in the next chapter represents several "types" of number, with "infinite" being what I believe it represents here, for the number of *ways* (*tera'iq*: "ways, roads, paths"). The verse then associates a *creation* with these ways and mentions how the god is not unaware of those living in, or occupying, such ways. Linguistically, *tera'iq* also implies a stacking, meaning that these ways or paths are stacked on top of each other (or ⟵ increase consecutively in number). Using my previously proposed logic, *tera'iq* can be interpreted as representing different dimensions or perhaps even representing different "worlds," since the Quran has clearly alluded to these places containing a great many of the god's creation (otherwise, the verse would not have called out how the god was not *ghafil*: "inattentive, unmindful, unaware"). The possibility of the existence of many more worlds "out there" is something that many scientists have proposed, in that we may be living in a universe that is nothing more than a "bubble" within perhaps an infinite number of other bubbles in the grander "multiverse" we may inhabit. Scientists have also speculated that the fundamental laws of physics or even the fundamental constituents of matter that have thus far defined our existence in our universe may in fact turn out to be different for each bubble. What a curious world we live in![94]

A Note about Translation Differences I

In this section, I want to touch on an important point with regard to the specific interpretations I present in this book. Some readers may not accept that the Quran provides modern-day, natural world insights and reject the conclusions arrived at in this book on the grounds that a number of different interpretations have been offered for the verses discussed in Part 3. Furthermore, these readers may feel that the interpretations presented here are not entirely credible because they have been specifically chosen to directly support the book's conclusions.

While it's perfectly appropriate to interpret a particular verse in several ways, what is *not* acceptable is for any of these interpretations to be linguistically invalid. One of the key messages I want to communicate in this

94. No one has proven the existence of a multiverse, so its existence is scientific conjecture today.

✳ *a hierarchy*

book is that common translations and interpretations for many science-related verses of the Quran are in fact erroneous, partly because they are not linguistically valid. I will use verse 67:19 presented in the Asteroid Belt section and verse 36:38 from the Limited Lifetime of Our Sun section to illustrate this point.

If you open up a common Quranic translation of verse 67:19, you'll read something like this:

> *Do they not see [or observe] the birds above them next to each other, spreading their wings and folding them in? No one can hold them except God [or Allah], the gracious [or merciful].*

Compare the above to my translation of the same verse:

> *Do they not extend their sights to the fliers above them forming a line and [or while] they jerk. No one can hold them except the one filled with mercy.*

These two translations are markedly different from each other, and it would be difficult for anyone to read the first one and agree with my conclusion that verse 67:19 provides important modern-day scientific insight. More seriously, though, the first translation makes little sense, and presenting it to an intelligent person who is not familiar with the Quran as "what God says, literally" will draw a response that probably ranges anywhere from a polite, dismissive smile to outright rejection of *anything* that comes from the Quran. So, let's closely dissect the original Arabic verse and see how the first translation did not do it justice.

Let's start by examining the words I translate as "extend their sights to," which are commonly translated as "see." As noted previously, the literal translation of the original Arabic is "see to" (or "see up to"). The original verse could have easily omitted the explicitly called-out "to," thus maintaining a simpler, more concise structure while keeping the same meaning. One of the points I make in this book is that words that appear extraneous in the Quran are clues to deeper meaning. When we humans talk casually among ourselves and add or delete a word, we don't think too much about it. However, when this is done in the Quran, we *must* think about it. And so, when I note the word "to" in the verse, I interpret this as an *extension* of sight and not just "seeing."

Let's next explore the word I translate as "flier." As I stated earlier in the section, "bird" is a common and accepted meaning, but it is not the *root* meaning of the word. The root of the word is *tar* ("to fly, to fly away, take wing"), which is also the root word for the Arabic word for "airplane" today.

Clearly, airplanes are not birds; they are "fliers." The common translation erroneously assumes that *tayr* only translates into "bird" because these were the only things that were known to "fly" up to about one hundred years ago.

Next, let's talk about the word *yek'bith*, which I translate as "jerk" and which is commonly translated as "birds folding their wings." Of course, we can see how the majority of translators translate the Arabic word into such an expression given they assume that the verse is talking about birds. But again, the common translation ignores the meaning of the root word for *yek'bith, qa'buth,* which *Al-Mawrid* translates as "to grasp, grip, or hold."

Finally, the original Arabic for the word I translate as "filled with mercy," is *the Rahman*, which, as I stated in chapter 1, is usually translated as the "merciful, kind, or compassionate" one. However, the expressive form for this word denotes an exaggeration of the root word that, as I also noted in chapter 1, means "the womb." Because of this, the Rahman should not be translated as "gracious" or "the one with mercy" but more accurately as "the one with *much* mercy."[95]

Another example illustrating linguistic shortsightedness by common translations comes from verse 36:38, which we examined in the Limited Lifetime of Our Sun section. We noted the use of the word *tejri* in that verse, which I argued means a running through time, not space. However, if you examine other translations, you will find authors translating *tejri* as "[the sun] runs in her course." As discussed before, the original verse never associated a spatial attribute with this running, so we cannot presume the existence of a "course," even though such a presumption is perhaps completely reasonable. Thus, "runs" and "runs in her course," although appearing to mean the same thing, in fact do not.

The tendency of many Quranic translators to ignore one or more of an original Arabic verse's words, letters, or overall structure is fairly common and results in many science-related verses of the Quran losing their intended scientific insight. Let's reexamine the first part of verse 36:38, which has been commonly translated as:

And the sun runs in her stable course.

While my translation for the same segment is:

And the sun runs to a stable state [or end, finish] for her.

In both translations, the important words "sun," "runs," "her," and "stable" have been preserved when translating from the original Arabic. However,

---

95. *Al-Mawrid* translates the Rahman as the "one with most mercy."

the original verse's linguistic structure has been changed in the common translation. This change of structure, which on the surface appears rather benign, has nonetheless caused the meaning of the verse to change from one that provides important scientific insight (the limited lifetime of our sun) to one that provides no scientific insight at all, in that the verse can now be interpreted as stating that the sun follows regular paths in the sky between its rising and setting, something known to humanity since we first appeared on Earth. To illustrate how the common translation has changed the original verse's structure, I need to provide a transliteration of the original Arabic in the exact same sequence as the original verse, along with word-for-word and letter-for-letter translations:

> *Weh [and] el [the] shamsu [sun] tejri [runs] lee[to] musta'qir [stable, settled, steady, constant, quiet] leh [for] ha [her].*

It's obvious from this transliteration that the translation I provided better communicates the original Arabic, and, more importantly, preserves its intended scientific insight. Although I will not have similar discussions for every science-related verse in Part 3, I wanted to delve into this topic here to note that the translations and interpretations presented in this book have been carefully chosen to preserve the original Arabic's words, letters, and structure, thus presenting translations that are not only linguistically valid but linguistically *accurate* as well. This accuracy is of prime importance given the linguistic richness and complexity of the Arabic language in general and of the Quran in particular.

6 The Earth Sciences

The time has come for us to leave the majestic cosmos behind and return to our home planet, Earth. In this chapter I discuss the numerous verses of the Quran that pertain to Earth sciences. As I did within each of the sections of chapter 5, I'll start by providing a background discussion that summarizes the established scientific belief, follow by listing the respective verses of the Quran for each topic, and conclude by presenting arguments that substantiate the agreement between science and the Quran. We will discover throughout the course of the chapter that the Quran has made many scientifically accurate statements within the realm of Earth sciences that would have been impossible for anyone living fourteen hundred years ago to have known. As was the case for the topics presented in chapter 5, the majority of the scientific discoveries cited in this chapter were made only very recently in human history.

Before going any further, though, let me briefly summarize the accepted scientific view of how planet Earth came to be.

Earth's Creation

Earth was created shortly after the birth of our sun and the subsequent formation of our solar system almost 5 billion years ago. Scientists today believe that our solar system formed after a star became a supernova (recall our discussion of black holes in chapter 5) at about that time and, in the process, released the gas, dust, and chemical elements that became the building blocks of our sun and of all the planets and various objects that make up our solar system today.

Planet Earth was formed by a process called accretion. Accretion takes place when relatively small bodies aggregate and stick to each other, mostly through the force of gravity, and form larger bodies called planetesimals. These planetesimals continue to aggregate over time, becoming even larger in size and turning into bodies called protoplanets. By attracting yet more nearby matter, the protoplanets continue to grow larger and larger over millions or tens of millions of years and form the rocky planets.[96] The

---

96. Planets can also be made entirely out of gas, such as the planets Jupiter and Saturn.

end result of this process is probably similar to how a snowball is made larger by gradually adding and squeezing more and more snow onto the initial lump. And so Earth formed by becoming larger and larger in size (and mass) as the force of gravity attracted more and more matter onto the growing young planet. There is a rather interesting fact to note here, though, as scientists believe that the timing of when the sun ignited was rather crucial to the later formation of Earth and of subsequent life on it.

As our sun ignited and turned into a star (not every large ball of gas becomes a star), much of the matter present in the region of the inner solar system was swept away. By this point, however, Earth had grown large enough in size (and mass) that it was not affected by the force that resulted from the sun's ignition. Had this ignition taken place prior to the planetesimals (the bodies that later formed Earth) growing relatively large in size and mass—thereby resisting the force that accompanied the sun's ignition—neither our planet nor we would be here now!

Earth was also fortunate enough to have formed in the part of the solar system known as the "habitable zone." A star's habitable zone signifies a particular distance from the star where a planet's surface temperature is not too hot and not too cold. This is important because, as we'll discuss in greater depth in the next chapter, it means that water can remain in a liquid state for very long periods of time—an absolute precondition to life as we know it. It turns out that the habitable zone for our star, the sun, is between 0.95 and 1.15 astronomical units.[97] This means that had Earth formed 5 percent closer to the sun or 15 percent farther away, it may not have been able to become the Earth we know today, nor would it have been able to harbor and foster life.

During Earth's early history, about 40 million years after it had formed, a Mars-size planet (Mars is about half the size of Earth) collided with Earth at a speed of some twenty thousand miles per hour. Fortunately for us, this collision was not head-on but was instead somewhat of a glancing blow. The collision nonetheless caused a substantial amount of debris to be ejected into space, which ultimately aggregated under the force of gravity and resulted in the formation of our moon. Scientists also believe that the exact angle and speed of this impact were crucial to our moon forming in the manner in which it did and to the moon assuming its specific attributes (most notably its size) that greatly influenced Earth's and life's subsequent progress and evolution.[98] Many scientists believe that from that point on ~

---

97. One astronomical unit is equal to the distance between Earth and the sun, or about 93 million miles.

98. Our moon is unique in the solar system in being relatively large compared to the size of its host planet.

the moon has played a crucial role in the emergence of life on our planet, with some having gone as far as saying that complex life itself would not have evolved on Earth without it. The collision that created the moon was also responsible for giving our planet its four seasons, as Earth's axis of rotation tilted from 0 to 23.5 degrees because of the force of the collision.

Earth was a very hot and inhospitable place shortly after it accreted and had no oceans, atmosphere, or continents. As Earth cooled, however, its internal layers, known as the crust, mantle, and core, began to form. Earth also began to excrete substantial amounts of gases from its surface and interior through degassing, a process that resulted in the creation of Earth's first atmosphere. As Earth further cooled, these gases condensed (changed from the gas state to the liquid state) into rain that, over many millions of years, resulted in the formation of Earth's earliest oceans. Scientists today believe that these oceans formed as early as 4.3 billion years ago but that they might have been subject to multiple cycles of evaporation and condensation due to frequent asteroid and large body bombardment of Earth during this early period in the planet's history.

At some point around 4 billion years ago, scientists believe that Earth's surface was either completely or almost completely covered with water. From that point in time onward, Earth was bombarded much less frequently, and the planet assumed some measure of stability that allowed early life to form, about 500 million years after the formation of Earth itself. Sometime after this (about 2.5 to 3 billion years ago) and largely due to a surge in volcanism, continental rock began to rise above the oceans due to density differences between this rock and deeper rock layers of Earth, and so land emerged as the continental rock "floated" on top of the deeper and denser oceanic rock.[99] With this brief introduction to the first several billion years of Earth's history, let's now examine the following verses:

> *[to Muhammad] Tell them: "You deny the one who created Earth in two days and you equate him with other gods. That is the god, the life giver of all worlds [or existences]." And he [the god] made in her [Earth or the land] anchors from a top, and blessed her, and estimated her sustenance in four days, provided equally to those who ask. **And then** he approached the sky while she is smoke [or vapor] and said to her and to Earth [or the land]: "Come together willingly or unwillingly," and they replied: "We come willingly." So he deemed them*

---

99. Continental rock is mostly granite, the same type of rock that your kitchen countertop may be made from, and oceanic rock usually consists of a type of basalt, a fine-grained, dark, dense rock.

seven skies in two days, and inspired [or provided] for each
sky her purpose [or function], and we made the lower sky
beautiful with lights [or lamps] and as a protection. That is the
estimation [or calculation] of the one filled with strength and
knowledge.

(41:9–12)

Reading through these verses, you can get a glimpse of how difficult interpreting the Quran can be at times! Beyond understanding that there is something called "the god" and that he is strong and knowledgeable, there is little else that makes sense in these verses. Nevertheless, if you read an interpretation for these verses—any interpretation of the Quran for these verses—you will find an attempt to explain them. I have yet to come across an interpretation in which the author or authors honestly state that they do not know what these verses really mean. Instead, scholars generally seem to feel obligated to interpret each and every verse in the Quran as if its meaning is, or must be, completely understood. While this may sound somewhat trivial, it can cause an incorrect interpretation to run counter to established science, thus making the very essence of the Quran come under question. In a similar vein, Muslims must consider and accept the fact that many verses in the Quran—science or otherwise—are in all likelihood misinterpreted, and such interpretations must be discarded in lieu of correct ones—a conclusion I embraced many years ago and one I'll bring up again in chapter 7 when discussing the evolution of life on our planet.

With respect to the verses at hand, some interpreters in recent times have understood the smoke or vapor mentioned to be interstellar gas and dust, from which the early solar system and other cosmic systems were formed. Scholars have also generally interpreted the lights or lamps mentioned to be the stars and planets in the sky. With respect to *days*, older interpretations assumed that Earth was created in two Earth days. However, as the age of Earth became better known in recent times, a few scholars have promoted the idea that these days should not be understood to be Earth days since the Quran explicitly states in other places that not all days are equal in length.[100] All in all, no one has yet offered a convincing explanation for these verses as far as I'm aware, but I'll nonetheless attempt to do so—correctly, I hope—in the next few pages.

When I first started to ponder these verses in preparation for writing

---

100. The Quran talks of some days equaling a thousand years (32:5), while others equal fifty thousand years (70:4), and yet others are like a thousand years (22:47), thus alluding to how time is relative. This is in agreement with Einstein's theory of relativity, proposed in the early twentieth century.

this book, I remember thinking that there was little hope of coming up with any good explanation, let alone the correct and intended one. Also, having lived in the United States for most of my life, I was well aware of the ridicule the six-day creation event had received, and this further solidified my mental doubts. Then one day, as I was lying on the bed staring at the ceiling, an idea suddenly flashed in my head. I immediately jumped up and grabbed my circa 1987 Hewlett Packard 28C college calculator (yes, it still works like it did the first day I bought it). I pressed in a few numbers and could not believe what I was seeing!

I knew that the age of the universe is known with a high degree of confidence to be 13.7 billion years old. I also knew that the age of Earth was known with similarly high confidence to be 4.54 billion years old. So I divided the age of Earth by that of the universe and then repeated the calculation—only now, I divided the number two by the number six. And it was the degree to which these two results agreed with each other that I found completely, but pleasantly, surprising. The first result expressed to three decimal places is 0.331. The second result, also expressed to three decimal places is 0.333. As you can see, these two numbers are fairly close to each other, and when I carried out these calculations, I thought their closeness represented more than a mere coincidence. But before I continue, I need to explain the significance of the number six.

There are many verses in the Quran that describe how the god created "the heavens and Earth" (the universe, in my mind) in six days. However, as noted earlier, the Quran also describes in select verses that not all days are, or should not understood to be, equal in length. We should therefore interpret these six days not as six Earth days but as some undetermined length of time.[101] I decided to use the known age of the universe to represent the number six. I also assumed that a creation, as described in these verses, signifies a time period from the beginning of the creation event (or Earth's accretion in this case) to when the Quran was revealed in time (effectively our present day), since "creation" is an ongoing process. Therefore, the two days mentioned in the verses corresponded to a period that started when Earth initially formed and ended when the Quran was revealed fourteen hundred years ago, a period we understand today to be 4.54 billion years, the age of Earth. Earth's point of accretion in time seems to also be the point of reference for the other two time periods mentioned in the verses, or at least it appears to provide a start time that yields a consistent and scientifically accurate interpretation for the three time periods.

So now we have six days representing 13.7 billion years, the two days

---

101. It can probably be argued that what's important is not the number six per se but what the ratios of two to six and four to six represent, as we'll see shortly.

mentioned in the verses representing 4.54 billion years, and the results I previously stated for the ratios of 4.54 to 13.7 and 2 to 6 illustrate how close these ratios are. Of course, the exact age of the universe may be slightly more or slightly less, and the same goes for the age of Earth. However, these "errors" are fairly small, so the close agreement between the two ratios remains valid.[102]

Using this same rationale, four days equates to 9.13 billion years, the period that also starts with Earth's accretion. The verses state that this four-day period corresponds with *blessing* (from *ba'rek*: "blessed, congratulated") *Earth and estimating* (from *qed'der*: "estimated, assessed") *her sustenance* (*uq'wat*: "food, nourishment"). The question here, however, is sustenance for what? I believe that this sustenance applies to "life" and to the length of time this life remains present on Earth. Life clearly requires sustenance, and the verses further say *provided equally* (*sawa'a*: "equal, alike") *to those who ask* (*sa'il*: "asker, inquirer"), which I interpret as meaning all of life's past, present, and future living species. Is this 9.13-billion-year time frame representative of how long life remains on Earth?[103]

This is a question that no one can answer today, but we can, nonetheless, speculate about life's potential duration based on established science. Scientists believe that life on Earth started about 4 billion years ago. It's also well accepted that life has proven to be quite resilient and that it can adapt rather quickly to dramatic changes in the larger environment. Additionally, scientists continue to find life in places on Earth where life "should not exist," thus substantiating life's survival power. However, it's also well accepted that our planet is ultimately controlled by a star, our sun, and this sun will run out of its fuel in approximately 5 billion years, as we discussed in chapter 5. As that end date nears, the sun will grow larger and larger until it literally "fries" Earth. Because of this, scientists believe that life will simply cease to exist, unable to continue under such extreme conditions. We can therefore crudely estimate life on Earth to continue until that time, which is not too far from our 4.6-billion-year estimate implied by the verses at hand.[104]

102. Based on knowledge of the age of the universe from Wilkinson Microwave Aniso-tropy Probe (WMAP) observations, its age has been determined to be between 13.64 and 13.86 billion years, while the estimate of 4.54 billion years for the age of Earth is accurate to within 1 percent.

103. This time frame implies that life will remain present on Earth for 4.63 billion years into the future, since it started about 4 billion years ago, 500 million years after Earth accreted (9.13 minus 4 minus 0.5 equals 4.63).

104. Scientists believe that as the sun grows larger and larger in size during its red giant phase, it will shed mass and this will cause Earth to move farther away from the growing sun, thus perhaps maintaining a safe distance for life on Earth for an extended period of time.

The verses then talk about how the sky was *smoke* (*dukhan*: "smoke, vapor").[105] As stated earlier, many interpreters thought this smoke to be the nebular gas and dust that eventually formed stars and galaxies. Such meaning is incorrect, though, since the verses clearly state that this smoke occurred after Earth's creation. This smoke must be interpreted then as the gases emanating from the cooling Earth in the degassing process described earlier and that clearly started some time (tens of millions of years) after Earth accreted (remember that 40 million years after Earth accreted, the collision with the Mars-sized planet took place, and it must have been a while after this that Earth began to gradually cool, excreting gases in the process).

We now know, based on established science, that our current atmosphere evolved over quite a long period of time, and Earth's current atmosphere is actually referred to by scientists as a "third generation" atmosphere. This evolution spanned a period of billions of years from shortly after Earth coalesced 4.5 billion years ago to about 420 million years ago, when ozone (one of the atmospheric layers or one of the "seven skies" mentioned in the Quran) reached sufficient quantities to allow life to move from the oceans to land. In addition to ozone, oxygen was essentially nonexistent in Earth's earliest atmosphere, and it too required almost 4 billion years after Earth's accretion before it reached its current atmospheric levels. In fact, only when life itself emerged did oxygen become available in the atmosphere through the photosynthesis process in which plants, with the aid of light from the sun, convert water and carbon dioxide into oxygen and energy-carrying organic molecules. We can therefore reasonably conclude that there also appears to be very good agreement between the two days mentioned by the verses for "establishing the seven skies" of the atmosphere and the length of time science tells us it took our current atmosphere to evolve (recall that each day in the verses represents 2.28 billion years).

There has also been quite a bit of confusion within the standard interpretation with regard to the apparent "discussion" between the god, Earth, and the sky. The standard interpretation assumes that the god is asking Earth and the sky to come to him together *willingly* (*tow'an*: "willingly, readily") *or unwillingly* (*ker'hen*: "unwillingly, reluctantly"). This interpretation makes little logical sense in my opinion, let alone no scientific sense whatsoever. Instead, what I believe the verses are referring to is the coming together of Earth and the early atmosphere. The reference the verses make to *willingly or unwillingly* probably pertains to a force that is either attractive or repulsive and is most likely an electromagnetic force, such as lightning.[106] The

---

105. The words *and then* bolded in the verses should be understood to start from the same point of reference we've used thus far, Earth's accretion.

106. Within the rules of electromagnetism, similar charges repel, while opposing charges attract, and lightning takes place because of a large potential difference

verses report that the answer that comes back is *we come willingly*, meaning that an attractive force is established and maintained.[107] In any case, the verses talk about the sky becoming seven skies in two days, and that each sky was given a particular *purpose* or *function* (*um'r*: "condition, state, directive"). This too is in agreement with current scientific understanding that the layers of the atmosphere are quite different from each other and that each layer plays an important role in maintaining our planet's health or otherwise serves some useful purpose (more on this later). The verses then go on to describe how the lower sky was *made beautiful* (*zay'yen*: "adorned, decorated") *with lamps* (*musabeeh*: "lamps, lights"). What are these lamps?

These lamps possibly refer to the lights of the auroras, seen from Earth's higher latitudes (the aurora borealis in the north and the aurora australis in the south), which result from Earth's magnetosphere (our magnetic shield) interacting with the solar wind (very energetic charged particles) emanating from our sun. These lights are—as most of us have seen on TV or, if fortunate, in person—indeed breathtaking, in agreement with the Quran's description as *beautiful*. It's also interesting to note here that in another verse (37:6), the Quran uses language when referring to these lights that can be interpreted as "the lights of the planets" (*el-kewakib*: "the planets"). I mention this because scientists have recently discovered that aurora lights are also present (in fact, they are visible from very far away) on other planets in our solar system, most notably the planets Jupiter and Saturn, due to their strong magnetic fields.

The verses then go on to say that the lower sky was made *to protect* (*hifth*: "preserve, protect"). This too is in agreement with science, as scientists have discovered that our atmosphere provides vital protection to life on Earth. For example, ozone in the atmosphere protects from harmful (and sometimes deadly) ultraviolet radiation. The magnetosphere also protects Earth from the solar wind as well as from "cosmic rays" that can come from the sun or from other places in the universe (such as from powerful supernova explosions). With reference to the magnetosphere, it's interesting to note how the verses associate the *lights* with the function of protection. The lights of the auroras are indeed a direct byproduct of the solar wind interacting with the magnetosphere, which is clearly playing a vital life protection role for Earth. Finally, Earth's atmosphere protects the planet from many falling comets and asteroids by burning them up

---

between the opposing charges of Earth's surface and the clouds.

107. The reference may instead be to the force of gravity, also an attractive force, and responsible for holding Earth's atmosphere in place and not allowing it to escape into space.

prior to their impact on Earth's surface. Without this critical atmospheric protection, life would simply have been unable to advance to the degree it has (or even been unable to survive).

Earth's Spherical Shape

We all accept Earth to be round today, as evidenced by so many beautiful pictures of our blue-green planet taken by satellites far above Earth's surface. However, this spherical shape has only recently become widely accepted.

Perhaps the earliest reports of a possible spherical shape for Earth are thought to have come from Pythagoras sometime around the sixth century BCE. There are also reports that Aristotle provided observational evidence of a spherical Earth around the year 330 BCE. It's also well known today that a man named Eratosthenes, who lived in Egypt around 240 BCE, ingeniously calculated Earth's circumference with a surprising degree of accuracy. Beyond these individual efforts and particular time and geography, however, there is ample evidence to suggest that many ancient and later civilizations believed Earth to be flat, as was the case in China, for instance, where this was an accepted truth up until the seventeenth century. The Quran has pointed to Earth's spherical shape through the following verse:

> *[The god] created the skies [or heavens] and Earth through [or by] Haqq. [He] encircles the night over the day, and encircles the day over the night, and [the god] put to your [humanity's] use the sun and the moon, all runs to a preset [or predestined] time.*
>
> (39:5)

This verse talks about how the night and day encircle each other. However, the Arabic word for *encircle* (*yuko'wir*: "to roll, ball, conglobate") is one normally associated with "a sphere." In fact, the Arabic words commonly used today for soccer, *kurat el-qadam*, translate to "the foot's ball," and the word "ball" (*kurat*: "ball, sphere, globe") derives from the same origin as the Arabic word for *encircle* in this verse.

Earth's Atmospheric Layers

In the first section of the chapter, I touched on how Earth's atmosphere evolved over a long period of time into the layered atmosphere it is today. I'll elaborate on this by providing a more in-depth discussion of Earth's atmosphere along with each layer's function, or *purpose*, as pointed out by the Quran. Scientists today believe that Earth's atmosphere consists of the following layers and associated functions:

- **The troposphere** This is Earth's nearest atmospheric layer and extends about eleven miles (18 km) from Earth's surface. Earth's weather occurs in this layer, and the troposphere is where the majority of naturally occurring, Earth-insulating greenhouse gases reside. Unlike the greenhouse gases caused by human emissions, these naturally occurring greenhouse gases are vital for the health of our planet.

- **The tropopause** This is a transition layer or boundary zone between the troposphere and the stratosphere. The tropopause does not maintain uniform height between Earth's tropics and poles, and this "structure" is important because it influences atmospheric circulation and the locations of the jet stream and polar front.

- **The stratosphere** This layer extends from about eleven miles (18 km) to about thirty-one miles (50 km) above Earth's surface. Ozone is located in this layer, which as noted earlier, is crucial to the protection of life on our planet.

- **The mesosphere** This layer extends from about thirty-one miles (50 km) to fifty miles (80 km) above Earth's surface. The upper part of this layer, known as the mesopause, constitutes the "coldest place on Earth," with temperatures that can approach -150° F. Scientists believe that the mesosphere plays an important role in global atmospheric circulation. This layer also contains Earth's highest clouds, which are virtually impossible to see with the naked eye.

- **The thermosphere (and ionosphere)** This layer extends from about fifty miles (80 km) to about four hundred miles (640 km) above Earth's surface. It's also within this layer that the auroras, or northern and southern lights, occur. Additionally, due to the fact that many ions (ions are atoms that carry a net electric charge) and free electrons (called *plasma* in this case) reside in this layer, radio waves (which are part of the electromagnetic spectrum of light) are reflected back to Earth, allowing short-wave radio communication possible between distant locations on its surface. Such communication has grown into a huge hobby for many of Earth's inhabitants over the years and has come to be known as amateur or "ham" radio.

- **The exosphere** This layer extends many thousands of miles above Earth's surface and is the outermost atmospheric layer that separates Earth from space.

We can see that Earth's atmosphere is rather complex and plays an important role in Earth's ability to nurture and support life. Furthermore, the layered structure of Earth's atmosphere plays a vital role in preventing Earth from "dehydrating." This is because the extremely cold tropopause and mesopause layers trap water vapor below, and this trap prevents solar radiation from breaking the water molecules into their constituent atoms of hydrogen and oxygen. Because hydrogen is a very light element, it can easily escape Earth's gravity and dissipate into space. Should this have occurred over any extended period of time, Earth might have lost its water along with its ability to support and nurture life.

With this general understanding of our atmosphere, let's now examine the following verses:

> *He [the god] is the one who created all that is on Earth [or the land] for you [humanity] and then turned to the sky and made it seven skies, and he is filled with knowledge about all things.*
> (2:29)

> *Did you [humanity] not see how the god created seven skies stacked on top of each other, and he made the moon within them as a light [or bright object], and made the sun as a lamp?*
> (71:15–16)

> *And we [the god] built on top of you [humanity] seven pulled [or tightened] ones.*
> (78:12)

The general interpretation of these verses has been somewhat problematic in the past because it was not clear what *sky (sema'a)* or *skies* referred to. Some have understood these skies to be the planets within our solar system, while others assumed they were different galaxies within the larger universe. In my mind, however, all these verses are referring to Earth's original and later atmospheres. If this is in fact the case, then the verses clearly allude to how Earth's atmosphere is a layered one, as has been confirmed by science. However, the verses also mention the number seven, so let me note a few things about how the Quran has used the number seven.

The number seven is used within the Quran to represent one of three "types" of numbers. The first type represents "the infinite," or a quantity that does not end. The second type represents "exactly the quantity seven." And the third type represents a quantity that is "many, but like seven."[108] No other number has been used by the Quran to represent anything other than its accepted numerical quantity. It therefore becomes important when trying to interpret a verse that contains the number seven to understand exactly what type of number seven represents in that particular instance.

I listed six layers in the beginning of the section (seven layers if we count

---

108. Verses 31:27, 12:47, and 9:80 represent examples of *seven* used as the "the infinite," "exactly seven," and "many, but like seven" types, respectively.

the thermosphere and ionosphere as two layers), but if you separate ozone as its own distinct layer (since it clearly possesses a distinct and useful purpose), then we get eight layers. However, not everyone considers the tropopause to be a distinct layer, so now we go back to seven (assuming we still count ozone as a layer). Some have also proposed that the magnetosphere should be considered its own layer, since it provides a crucial protective function for life on Earth against the solar wind. Thus, we can see that a certain degree of arbitrariness is involved in trying to quantify the exact number of Earth's atmospheric layers. This is why I believe the number seven in these verses should be interpreted as representing the "many, but like seven" type of number. What the Quran is stating is that Earth has a number of *skies*, or atmospheric layers, and that these layers add up to about seven, in agreement with the scientific understanding of Earth's layered atmosphere.

Let's now turn our attention to the second group of verses. This group mentions something curious with respect to the moon being part of the seven skies. This group conflicts with the explanation I just provided, since the moon is currently located some 250,000 miles (400,000 km) away from Earth, outside of even the outer limits of the exosphere. As a matter of fact, it was because of this group of verses that most interpreters have proposed *skies* to be celestial skies that go far beyond Earth (such as planets or galaxies), since the Quran clearly mentions the moon as part of them. In early readings of these verses, I remember noting how the Quran seemed to include the moon as part of the skies but not the sun. This struck me as odd, although I did not understand why at the time. It turns out, however, that a long time ago the moon was much closer to Earth than it is today.

As was described in the first section of this chapter, the moon formed when a Mars-size planet collided with Earth shortly after Earth formed, 4.5 billion years ago. This collision marked the birth event for our moon, which formed as the debris from this collision coalesced under the force of gravity over a period of time. When this happened, however, the moon was located only 14,000 miles (nearly 23,000 km) away from Earth's surface, much closer than its present position. What's not clear today, however, is how far above Earth's surface the early atmosphere of Earth extended when the moon formed. We do know that Earth's current theoretical limit for the exosphere is more than 100,000 miles (160,000 km) above Earth's surface. This theoretical limit is where the influence of solar radiation pressure on the velocities of atomic hydrogen atoms (a component of our atmosphere) exceeds Earth's gravitational pull. A planet's gravitational pull on its atmospheric gases is crucially important, since these gases can and will escape into outer space if this gravitational pull is not strong enough. Scientists today believe that this was partly the reason why the planet Mars could not hold onto its atmosphere when it formed. In addition to its lack of a magnetic shield to protect against solar radiation, Mars simply was not massive enough to exert a strong enough pull to keep its atmosphere from escaping, a fate we on Earth were fortunate enough to escape (no pun intended).[109]

Even Earth's observable atmosphere (the outer limits of the exosphere) extends to about 60,000 miles (96,000 km) above Earth's surface. Such observation is possible from outer space as a "halo" around our planet called the *geocorona*. It's therefore not difficult to accept that the moon may have formed inside Earth's atmosphere, as noted by the Quran, especially since Earth excreted so much gas during that early period of its life. Another interesting point to make in this regard is the use of the word *how* (*kaif*: "how, in what way") in the second group of verses. These verses point the reader to examine how our atmosphere came to be. We now know that this was a process that spanned over billions of years, during which time the moon has also slowly receded away from Earth to its current position. The verses also describe the moon as a *light* or *bright object* (*noor*: "light, brightness, glow"). This is clearly the case today, especially with a full moon on a clear night, but this light was so much brighter when the moon first formed. Imagine the moon then, filling almost the entire night sky (as believed to have been the case). How bright this object must have appeared from Earth, given how close it was to the surface!

Finally, the third verse talks about *seven pulled (or tightened) ones* (*shee'dada*: "tightened, pulled, strong"). The use of *pulled* by the Quran is also an important and accurate choice that requires further discussion. As previously stated, the planet Mars could not hold onto its atmosphere because it was not able to create a large enough gravitational pull to keep its atmosphere from escaping into space. However, due to its larger size and heavy iron core, Earth fared much better, since our atmosphere remained tightly in place, allowing life to exist and evolve on its surface. Thus, in addition to indicating that Earth's atmosphere is a layered one, verse 78:12 also provides a direct reference to the force of gravity (as discussed in chapter 5) through the use of the word *pulled*.

---

109. Mars lost its magnetic shield due to its relatively small size, which accelerated the planet's cooling and led to the solidification of its liquid iron core, eliminating Mars's magnetic shield in the process (the motion or convection of the molten part of the core is what generates the magnetic field).

Earth's Internal Layers

Just as the Quran describes our atmosphere as layered, Earth is described by the Quran as containing many layers as well. Based on seismic wave analysis, scientists today believe that Earth's interior contains numerous layers, which formed as Earth cooled from its initial smoldering state. Scientists further believe that this layering process, or differentiation of Earth's interior into layers of differing densities that vary with depth, was possibly the most important event our planet experienced. However, as is the case with the atmosphere, there is no universal agreement on the exact number of Earth's layers, and this too seems to be subject to a certain degree of arbitrariness. The Quran describes Earth's layered structure in the following verse:

> *The god is the one who created seven skies, and of Earth [or the land] like them too.*
>
> (65:12)

As far as Earth's layers go, scientists universally agree that Earth contains three major layers. These are the crust (Earth's outermost layer), the core (Earth's innermost layer), and the mantle (located between the core and the crust). There's also universal agreement among scientists that the mantle layer is further divided into an upper mantle and a lower mantle and that the core layer also consists of a solid inner core and a liquid outer core. In addition to these major layers, scientists have discovered three boundary zones, or "discontinuities," which are classified as relatively thin layers that separate the major ones.

So as far as the count is concerned, we end up with between five and eight layers for Earth's interior. There is also no reason to believe that scientists won't alter their understanding of these layers in the future. Nevertheless, as is the case with the atmosphere, the Quran does not limit the count of Earth layers to exactly seven since the number seven could be understood to mean "many, but like seven" in this context as well. This rationale is further supported by the verse saying *like them too* (*mith'li*: "similar to, analogous to, same as").[110]

---

110. Some scholars have interpreted *of Earth* as pertaining to Earth's continents while others interpreted it as "other Earths" in the larger universe. However, if we accept the meaning of "seven skies" as the stack of Earth's atmospheric layers, then it's more reasonable to assume that the verse is describing Earth's interior layers since the verse establishes a parallel between these skies and Earth.

The Origin of Earth's Water

Where did Earth's water come from? This important question has puzzled scientists for a long time. Initially people believed that Earth's water came from outer space through ice-bearing comets and asteroids. It was also assumed that these objects bombarded the early Earth for tens or hundreds of millions of years, resulting in the formation of Earth's earliest oceans. Although popular for a while, this view has been challenged by a number of scientists as a result of several recent discoveries.

First, when scientists analyzed the type of water from some comets, they discovered that this water was different from the type of water on Earth.[111] Scientists also discovered that most of the early bombardment of Earth was from dry asteroids and not from wet comets. And although some of Earth's water was delivered through this mechanism, scientists concluded that a different theory on the origin of water was needed, and so the "wet accretion" hypothesis was put forth. According to this new theory, Earth formed from water-containing materials already present in the inner solar system. In other words, the majority of Earth's water came from Earth and not from outer space. The Quran has alluded to this origin of Earth's water through the following verse:

> [The god] extracted from her [Earth] her water.
>
> (79:31)

The verse's use of *extracted from her* (*akh'raja*: "take out, bring out") clearly points to Earth's water as being indigenous in nature, in agreement with the wet accretion hypothesis.

The Lowest Place on Earth

A battle took place in the year 614 CE between a Persian army and a Byzantine (Roman) army led by Heraclius, historically verified to have taken place near the current area of the Dead Sea outside the city of Jerusalem. The Persians were the clear victors, and upon hearing of this victory, the Arab polytheists—the ones who initially vehemently rejected Muhammad, as noted in chapter 2—came to Muhammad and taunted him and his new faith. They claimed that if Muhammad was correct in preaching going back to one god, then the Byzantines, who were Christians and who worshipped the same one god, would not have been defeated at the hands of the Persians. (The Persians, like the Arabs, did not subscribe to the notion of one god.)

---

111. Scientists studied the comets Halley, Hyakutake, and Hale-Bopp during near-Earth passes made in 1986, 1996, and 1997, respectively.

This obviously distressed the prophet and the Muslims, and sometime between the years 615 and 620 the following verses were revealed:[112]

> [*The Arabic letters*] *"alif"-"lam"-"meem." Defeated were the Romans, in the lowest of Earth [or the land], but they shall be victorious after their loss, in several years.*
>
> (30:1–4)

First, I'll need to say a few things about the letters that started the verse, as I'm sure they may have caught your eye. These letters are an example of what's known as the "disjointed letters" within the Quran, an aspect of the Quran that remains mysterious to this day.

About one-fourth of the chapters of the Quran begin with one or more disjointed letters. These letters are usually—but not necessarily—followed by an expression that typically takes the form "These are the signs of the clear book" (referring to the Quran). No one yet knows what the intention behind these letters is or what they are meant to signify. Scholars have put forth several explanations over the ages, but I do not believe that any of these explanations offer the true meaning behind these letters. Their explanations are rather superficial, in my view, with perhaps the most accepted one being that chapters with similar disjointed letters share common themes. Some have proposed that these letters signify the "building blocks" of the Quran, meaning that it's miraculous how something like the Quran can come from mere letters. Some have proposed they perhaps may reveal some curious mathematical relationships within the Quran, or they may even constitute some sort of a key (or code) that could unlock more levels of meaning or knowledge from the Quran. There are several more opinions regarding these letters, but, as I noted earlier, the verdict is most likely still out on what they represent. I think that uncovering the real intent behind these letters is probably one of the most exciting Quranic discoveries yet to be made.[113]

Turning back to the subject at hand, these verses clearly state that the battle that took place in 614 took place in *the lowest of Earth (or the land)*. Contrary to what some have suggested, the Arabic word for *lowest* (*edna:* "minimum, lowest, least") specifically translates into *lowest*, not *lower*. Also contrary to

---

112. Quranic historians do not agree on the exact date of when these verses were revealed, but all estimates fall within this range.

113. Some have proposed an even more mystical meaning for these letters in that they may refer to other names of the prophet Muhammad within other future worlds, since, in some cases, these letters allude to the god "calling Muhammad's name."

what others have claimed, this word cannot be translated as the "nearest land," since such a translation makes no logical sense, unless the point of reference is somewhere in the ocean, which is clearly not the case here. Instead, it has been scientifically verified that the area of the Dead Sea, at almost 1400 feet (424 m) below sea level, is the lowest place on our planet.

Oxygen Production through Photosynthesis and Oxygen's Role in Fire

One of the most important processes of life is photosynthesis. Through photosynthesis, plants, algae, and certain species of bacteria produce energy-carrying organic compounds (such as sugars) and oxygen from water and carbon dioxide, with the aid of energy from the sun in the form of sunlight. Photosynthesis is so important to life that nearly every living species derives its energy either directly or indirectly from it. Moreover, the oxygen that's required for respiration (breathing) and metabolism (converting food into energy) for a great many of Earth's species comes exclusively from the photosynthetic process. The Quran contains three verses that together allude to a key aspect of photosynthesis (oxygen production) as well as point out how this byproduct constitutes a critical component of fire. Let's examine these verses:

> *Do you [humanity] see the fire you kindle? Did you establish her tree, or are we [the god] the establishers?*
>
> (56:71–72)

> *The one [the god] who made for you [humanity], **from** the green tree, fire. So that from it [fire] you kindle.*
>
> (36:80)

These verses make mention of the known phenomenon of fire and, curiously, also associate the word *tree* with it. The fact that trees are burned in fire is something known for quite a long time, and if we interpret these verses as "trees becoming fires," then the Quran reveals nothing new or exciting here. To understand how this is not the case, let's examine closely the choice of words used by these three verses to consider whether the Quran is perhaps revealing something more insightful when it comes to how fires come about. But first, let's briefly go over the nature of fire.

Fires are produced when a chemical chain reaction takes place under a specific set of circumstances. Certain conditions must be met: the availability of a material that is flammable or combustible (aka the fuel), the availability of sufficient quantities of an oxidizer such as oxygen, and a temperature that exceeds the flash point of the fuel/oxidizer mix. If all these components are in place, a fire will start and will continue to persist as long as both fuel and oxidizer are available (which is why it's called a chain reaction).

The first set of verses talks about the *tree* (*sheh'jereh*) of fire. The standard interpretation of this verse presumes that this tree refers to the different tree types that can be used to start a fire, with some interpreters even specifying which types. Thus, the standard interpretation proposes that the god is asking humanity to reflect on how the god created trees and how these trees are used to create fires. This is, in my view, a somewhat flawed perspective because the verses use a singular form for *tree*, as opposed to the plural *trees*, which the Quran would have used if the reference is to the various tree types that produce fires. If we accept this reasoning, then the verses are clearly describing the "tree of fire" and how this tree becomes established. However, using the word *tree* to describe a fire is rather odd and is not a generally accepted or common linguistic practice in Arabic (also, the Quran does not associate *tree* with fire elsewhere). Furthermore, the word *tree* is somewhat redundant here, as the verses could have easily communicated the same meaning by saying "Do you [humanity] see the fire you kindle? Did you establish her or are we the establishers?" The verses, therefore, wanted to specifically call out *tree* and associate it with fire.

I believe such an association to be more than a mere coincidence. We know today that fires require oxygen, and we also know that oxygen in Earth's atmosphere is solely produced by plants through photosynthesis. In fact, Earth's atmosphere was absent any oxygen until life itself evolved enough complexity that certain species of bacteria, algae, and plants came onto the scene to produce it. So, by associating *tree* with fire, the verses may be referring to how trees ultimately produce fires, not because trees can act as "fuel" but because they produce oxygen gas, the other critical component of fire. This interpretation is further supported by verse 36:80, which, interestingly, also calls out the color *green* (*akh'thar*). The reference to green is quite telling, because we all know that green trees are usually alive, with a substantial portion of water within them, and thus do not burn as easily or as quickly as dead or dry ones do. So the second verse's use of *green* rather than *brown* or *yellow* is probably meant to provide further insight.

Let's now focus on this *green* aspect of trees. Trees (specifically tree leaves) are green in color because of a pigment called chlorophyll. This biomolecule absorbs all wavelengths (or colors) of light, but not the green wavelength, which is reflected back into our eyes when we see a green leaf or plant. Chlorophyll is also a vital component of the photosynthesis process. Without this *green*, there would be no photosynthesis and no oxygen production. Thus, what I believe verse 36:80 is stating is that fire comes from *green trees* not because the source of the fire (the fuel) is the green tree but because the green tree indirectly enables the phenomenon of fire through the production of oxygen, itself only made through the tree being *green*.

The next important key word to examine is the word *established* used in the first set of verses. As I point out throughout the book, the word *establish* (*insha'a*: "establish, bring into being, manufacture") takes on a very specific meaning within the Quran and almost always denotes some sort of elaborate process (chapter 9 discusses *establish* in greater detail). So, if we accept that the first set of verses is talking about the *tree of fire* (as opposed to trees that burn and produce fires), then the Quran is stating that fire is created by an elaborate process (the chemical chain reaction noted earlier) that is also associated with *trees*, in agreement with the role oxygen plays in starting and sustaining fires.

The next key word to note is the word *from* bolded in the second verse (*minn*). It's well accepted that fire doesn't come from trees. Leaves, seeds, and fruits come from trees, but not fire. So the Quran chose a rather curious linguistic structure that leads the reader to believe that the Quran is stating that fire does in fact somehow come from trees. This, in my view, further supports the interpretation that what comes from green trees to create fire, according to this verse, is really oxygen.

The Depletion of Ozone

While vacationing several years ago, I came across an interesting chapter from a book titled *It Must Be Beautiful*. The book aimed to present important mathematical equations that helped shaped modern human society and that also possessed a certain degree of elegance and beauty. The chapter that specifically caught my interest was about the so-called Molina-Rowland equations. These chemical equations were named after the two scientists, Mario Molina and F. Sherwood Rowland, who first discovered them. They summarized how the ozone molecule was being depleted from our upper atmosphere—specifically from the ozone-rich stratosphere—by synthetic chemical compounds called chlorofluorocarbons, or CFCs. The scientists published these equations in the prestigious science journal *Nature* in 1974. They then took on not only the then-powerful American chemical industry but the majority of doubting scientists as well. These doubters were hired by some powerful players within the chemical industry to challenge and refute the claims made by Molina and Rowland and to downplay any harm CFCs may have caused Earth's atmosphere.

The claim that Molina and Rowland made was that CFCs manufactured by the American chemical giants at the time were depleting Earth's ozone, which plays a vitally important role in maintaining the health of life on Earth.[114] It would take eleven years of bitter debate, during which the two scientists felt compelled to take their findings directly to the American public in a forum that was known as the "Incredible Stratospheric Travelling Road Show and Debating Society." This forum lasted for a period of two years, during which Molina and Rowland presented their case to other scientists, politicians, industry leaders, and the general public. Luckily for all Earthlings, these scientists were victorious in their quest to get people to understand the destructive effect these chemicals have, as evidenced by the ban on many CFC-carrying products today by many countries in the world.

I read this story prior to writing this book, and the memory of how difficult it was for these two well-meaning scientists to try to save life on Earth stuck in my mind. Years later, I reread a particular verse in the Quran and immediately realized that the Molina-Rowland story provided the appropriate context for its interpretation. Here's the verse:

> *And we [the god] made the sky a protected [or preserved] ceiling, and yet they are in denial of [or in opposition to, ignorance of] her signs [or indications].*
>
> (21:32)

Given the context of *a protected* (*mah'footh*: "preserved, protected") *ceiling* (*seqf*: "ceiling, roof") and *denying* (*i'rath*: "turning away from, shunning, renouncing") *her signs* (*eye'yat*: "signs, indications"), I believe that here *sky* (*sema'a*) must refer to Earth's lower atmosphere, which is protected in part by the ozone shield located in the stratosphere. I also interpret the signs being denied as referring to the context of the Molina-Rowland discovery and the subsequent "battle" between these two scientists and their opponents. Clearly, according to this verse, there is some sort of major denial, disagreement, or opposition going on with respect to these signs, which I thought could not have applied to seventh-century Arabs denying any sky signs because no one knew then that the sky was "protected." And even if someone living fourteen hundred years ago realized that the sky provided some sort of protective function, no one would have any reason to deny that.

Some of you may feel that I'm using a specific, perhaps even tailored, interpretation for this verse that may or may not provide its intended meaning. This objection is valid on the surface, but does an alternative interpretation for this verse provide a more specific, or accurate, explanation?

---

114. It's interesting to note that prior to humans coming into the picture, ozone was naturally regulated by Earth, with ozone created at the same rate it was destroyed.

These verses do not specify what is meant by *sky*, who *they* are, or what is meant by *signs*. But does this lack of specification mean we can assign any interpretation we like?

Interpreting the Quran must be based on firm and concrete knowledge, and this knowledge may or may not be known or available to those interpreting the Quran at any one particular time. I believe that the Quran is a specific book that contains specific messages but that are wrapped at times in somewhat simple and general language. I don't believe the Quran intends to create an atmosphere of ambiguity or cause mass confusion but instead seeks to encourage reflection and further study in order to be able to correctly interpret and communicate its difficult-to-interpret verses as well as its true essence.

Decreasing Oxygen Intake with Altitude

Most of us have probably seen pictures on television or in magazines of mountain climbers at the top of Mount Everest, the highest peak in the world. Many of these climbers are also shown wearing an oxygen mask or some sort of apparatus to facilitate proper breathing at an altitude almost 29,500 feet (9000 m) above sea level. However, the percentage of oxygen in a fixed volume of air does not decrease with higher altitudes. Instead, air becomes less dense and atmospheric pressure drops fairly rapidly as climbers ascend higher and higher into the atmosphere. This rapid drop in pressure causes breathing to become more difficult because the mechanism that drives the flow of oxygen from our lungs to our bloodstream becomes weaker with this drop in pressure.[115] Associating breathing *difficulty* (*they'iq*: "narrow, tight, confined, restricted") with the act of *ascending* (from *yes'ad*: "climb, ascend, rise to") has been captured by the Quran through the following verse:

> And if [the god] wants to lead a person away from the path
> [of truth], he [the god] will constrict his chest with difficulty
> [breathing], as if ascending in the sky.[116]
>
> (6:125)

Although the city of Mecca, where Muhammad was born and raised, was

---

115. The atmospheric pressure drops due to the decreased density of air at higher altitudes; there are far fewer air molecules (and far fewer oxygen molecules, since oxygen is a component of air) in a given volume of air at higher altitudes than at sea level.

116. This verse should not be interpreted in the literal sense (as the god directly causing breathing difficulty); instead, the verse points to the general state of unease that accompanies being away from the path of truth (or virtue).

surrounded by mountains, these mountains were generally no more than a few thousand feet high. Thus, it's probably true that having severe difficulty breathing while climbing a mountain didn't occur in that environment. The verse furthermore talks about ascending in the sky, an experience absent anywhere on Earth fourteen hundred years ago.

Plate Tectonics and Mountain Formation

As stated back in chapter 3, one of the key discoveries made within the science of geology was the theory of plate tectonics. In a nutshell, Earth's crust was discovered to contain smaller landmasses called plates, similar to how a jigsaw puzzle contains many smaller pieces that fit together. These plates are further divided into major and minor plates. Earth's crust was found to contain seven or eight major plates and more minor plates. Also, these plates are not fixed to Earth but move horizontally according to a process known as convection, in which matter flows as a result of heat energy. During this flow, matter that is hot and less dense rises, while cooler and denser matter sinks. A quick and simple way to observe firsthand how convection works is by boiling water in a pot and placing a cork somewhere in the middle of the pot's opening. As the water begins to churn, the cork will start to move about the surface of the water, and this movement is in direct response to the process of convection.

Earth's interior is also very hot (because of what's known as radioactive decay), and this heat energy causes convection in Earth's mantle layer, which in turn causes the plates to slowly move at an average rate of a few centimeters per year—the same rate as the growth of your fingernails. As these plates come against each other and collide, mountain ranges form, and this direct result of plate tectonics is the process through which Earth's mountain ranges have formed. For instance, the Himalayas, the range home to Mount Everest, formed as a result of a collision between the Indian and Eurasian plates 55 million years ago, while similar plate collisions were responsible for forming the Alps in Europe and the Andes in South America.[117]

The story of the discovery of plate tectonics is quite interesting. In 1910, American geologist Frank B. Taylor proposed a radically new idea in which he claimed that Earth's mountain chains were the result of "continental drifting." However, this proposition was ignored by the scientific community, as no one was able to come up with a convincing mechanism that

---

117. In addition to becoming great structures, mountains diminish in size with the passage of time as a result of weathering. For instance, unlike their relatively modest heights today, the peaks of the Appalachian mountains of North America were Earth's highest mountain peaks around 500 million years ago.

would cause such drifting. Nevertheless, one scientist latched on to the idea, the German meteorologist Alfred Wegener, who was the first to show how the "fit" of various continents supported the idea that all the continents were once united in a single supercontinent. Wegener also used fossil records of various species to support his findings, which further demonstrated how landmasses can move apart over long periods of time. In spite of these new findings, geologists remained skeptical until the 1960s, when the confirmation of the theory of plate tectonics was made, which geologists and geophysicists have since universally accepted.[118] Scientists today believe that plate tectonics was so important to our planet that complex life itself would not have emerged in its absence.

The benefits of plate tectonics are too numerous to mention here, but the most important benefit is plate tectonics' role in maintaining a stable global surface temperature for our planet over billions of years. This temperature stability was quite important because life was given the opportunity to continue to evolve into forms of higher complexity without becoming wiped out and having to start all over again (assuming, of course, that it even could). And just like the universe's expansion was a hotly debated issue for a while until it was confirmed in the 1920s, so too was the theory of plate tectonics until it was confirmed in the middle of the twentieth century. In both instances, however, the Quran provided scientifically correct insight and did so many hundreds of years prior to these discoveries. Let's begin by examining the following verse:

> And [I, the god, swear] by Earth of the cracks [or faults].
>
> (86:12)

In this verse, the god swears by Earth, while stating that it contains *cracks* or *faults* (*sed'i*: "cracks, fissures, rifts, chasms, faults"), in agreement with what I described in the major and minor plates. Let's next examine the following verses:

> And [through] the mountains he [the god] anchored her [Earth or the land].
>
> (79:32)

> And the mountains are [like, as] stakes.
>
> (78:7)

---

118. The U.S. Navy takes the lion's share of the credit for this confirmation, following the navy's extensive global mapping of the oceanic floor, which clearly depicted the plate structure of Earth's crust.

*And we [the god] made in [or within] her [Earth or the land]
very tall anchors.*

(77:27)

*And the earth [or land] we [the god] stretched, and provided
her with [or implanted in her] anchors.*

(50:7)

*And we [the god] made in Earth [or the land] anchors so that
she does sway with them.*

(21:31)

*Or who made Earth [or the land] a calm [or restful] place, and
made rivers run through her, and gave her anchors.*

(27:61)

*And he [the god] set in Earth [or the land] anchors, so that she
does not sway with you [humanity], and rivers, and pathways,
hoping you [humanity] find your ways.*

(16:15)

In all these verses, the Quran implies that Earth (or more appropriately,
the land) moves, and this movement was stopped or anchored by mountains (*rawaseya*: "anchors"). It's also interesting to note that even though
mountains appear to us to be on top of Earth, all theses verses (specifically
the third, fifth, and seventh verses) use *in* (*fee*: "in, within") Earth and not
on Earth when referring to the action of anchoring. This particular insight
is further supported by the use of *stakes* (*aw'tada*: "pegs") by verse 78:7,
since we all know that stakes extend farther into the ground than what is
visible above the ground's surface, which is also true for mountains.

For quite some time prior to the confirmation of plate tectonics, the
popular belief among scientists was that mountains were nothing more
than wrinkles on Earth's crust following the planet's cooling and shrinking.
This explanation probably remained popular for so long because mountains
do appear to be on top of Earth. However, as the Quran accurately clarifies,
mountains are associated with the movement of land (the use of *anchors*
and *stakes* clearly implies motion or a tendency for something to move),
and they came from *in* Earth. The description by the Quran is in agreement
with our current scientific understanding of how mountains form deep in
Earth as plates move, collide against each other, and then cease to move in
the forward direction (i.e., become "anchored") as mountain chains form.[119]

119. Because of the significance of plate tectonics to our planet, this point bears em-

Let's next turn our attention to the fourth verse. This verse talks about how earth (or land) was *stretched* (*mu'det*: "extended, stretched, spread out"), and it associates such stretching with mountains. This, too, is in agreement with our current scientific understanding of a single, large landmass in the form of a supercontinent called Pangaea, which existed between 250 and 280 million years ago and was broken apart due to the action of plate tectonics to form the continents we see on any map of the world today. As these smaller landmasses collided, mountains resulted at the plate boundaries.

I also want to say a few things about the sixth verse. In this verse, the Quran talks about how the god made Earth a *restful* or *calm* place (*qarar*: "orderly, stable, calm, peaceful"). This statement is simple but very important and accurate. Earth *is* a very calm and livable place by planetary standards. On Earth, we don't have a runaway greenhouse effect, as is the case with our sister planet ,Venus, where temperatures soar to more than 800°F on the surface (almost twice that of an oven) as a result of Venus's lack of plate tectonics. On Earth, plate tectonics drives the recycling of the chemical element carbon, which in turn prohibits carbon dioxide gas (CO_2) from continuing to accumulate in the atmosphere, the primary reason for Venus's runaway greenhouse effect and why its atmospheric pressure is a crushing ninety times that of Earth's. On the planet Jupiter, a massive storm three times larger than Earth has been brewing nonstop, with winds of three hundred miles an hour and for more than three hundred years![120]

Venus and Jupiter fared better than Mars, which lost most of its atmosphere billions of years ago, making the existence and development of life on its surface a virtual impossibility. There are many more life-intolerant conditions and examples both from within and outside our solar system, and they all seem to point to how fortunate humanity has been in having had the opportunity to be part of this very hospitable and forgiving planet.[121]

A Note about Translation Differences II

Because the understanding regarding plate tectonics is, in my view, one of the most important scientific insights provided by the Quran, I want to

phasizing one more time: *no one* prior to the Quran or after its revelation (up until the early twentieth century) had proposed and documented a relationship between mountain formation and movement of land. And when a scientist proposed such a correlation, thirteen hundred years after the Quran, he was not taken seriously by the larger scientific community. Yet, the Quran described exactly such an association and did so in eight separate verses (see verses 41:9–12 in the beginning of the chapter).

120. Scientists believe that winds normally blow in excess of a thousand miles per hour on the planets Saturn and Neptune.

121. Because everything was "just right" for Earth, some scientists have dubbed it the Goldilocks planet.

discuss the differences between my translations and the translations of others and point out the errors in those earlier translations that have resulted in a number of the verses cited in this section losing their intended scientific insight. This discussion parallels a similar one provided in chapter 5, in which I discuss similar translation errors made in the "limited lifetime of the sun" and "asteroid belt" verses.[122]

Let's start with verse 86:12, which I translated as *And [I, the god, swear] by Earth of the cracks [or faults]*. A number of other translations have translated this verse as *And by the earth which cracks*. Clearly, these translations offer somewhat different meanings, but, more importantly, the common translation does not yield any scientific insight, since "earth cracking" has been observed prior to the Quran in situations of excessive heat and dryness, as well as when plants spring forth from the ground. So, as I did in chapter 5, let me provide an exact transliteration of the original verse to see why my translation is the more appropriate one:

> *Weh [by] el [the] ardh [Earth, the land] thaat [of] el [the] sud'i [cracks]*

As we can see, my translation preserves all the words, letters, and structure of the original verse as well as best communicates the meaning of the verse given the verse's use of the key word *thaat*. Al-Mawrid translates this word as "self, person, subject, being, essence, nature, the very same, the selfsame, the identical." We can see from this list of potential meanings for *thaat* that the Quran is clearly communicating the fact that *cracks* are part and parcel of Earth, one of its inherent qualities. The erroneous translation not only ignores the original verse's structure and lack of any words that can be translated into *which*, but it also overlooks the importance of the Quran's use of the word *thaat*.

The next aspect I need to discuss is the use of the word *rawaseya* by all the verses presented in this section (except verse 78:7, which uses *stakes*). A number of common translations have given this word as "firmly set," as opposed to my translation of *anchors*. The difference may appear insignificant on the surface, but it is actually huge because we cannot accept that these verses offer any scientific insight into plate tectonics if we understand mountains to be firmly set *on* Earth (something man has accepted since

---

122. I believe that many of the erroneously translated verses are so because they were interpreted in the absence of any scientific insight, and the interpretations were chosen because they were the only ones that yielded anything meaningful or logical in such an environment.

the dawn of time) as opposed to them being anchors *for* the earth (thus implying motion of land).

Let's examine *rawaseya* more closely. *Rawaseya*, or the equivalent *raseeyat*, is translated by *Al-Mawrid* as "unshakable mountains." These terms are the plural of *rassin*, which *Al-Mawrid* translates as "anchored, at anchor or firm, fixed, stable, firmly established." However, both *rawaseya* and *rassin* come from one root word, *ersa*, which *Al-Mawrid* translates as "to anchor, moor, berth, place at anchor." Thus, we can see that while translating *rawaseya* as "firmly set mountains" makes good logical sense, it is, nonetheless, a somewhat inaccurate translation as far as the verses we're discussing here are concerned. Clearly, there must be a good reason why these verses specifically chose the word *rawaseya*, and I believe this reason is to communicate an anchoring action of land that's in motion and that's taking place through the creation of mountains. The Quran could have chosen from a number of other words that can be used to better communicate mountains' apparent firmness, immovability, or stability, if indeed that was what all these verses had intended to communicate.

The next point I'll make concerns verse 79:32, which I translated as *And [through] the mountains he [the god] anchored her [Earth or the land]*. This verse has been commonly translated as *And the mountains he [the god] set firmly*. Again, the common translation does not support the verse providing any scientific insight. The point of discussion about this verse is that based only on verse 79:32, you cannot easily tell which translation is the correct one due to the verse's brevity, as illustrated through the following exact transliteration:

Weh [and] el [the] jibal [mountains] ersa [to anchor] ha [her].

This verse presents an example of how the common translation ignores general context and a verse's logical flow within a series of verses. Notice how the common translation does not make any reference to Earth, even though the general context *is* Earth. To see how this must be the correct context, I offer my translations of the previous two verses and the following verse (verses 79:30–79:33):

And Earth after that he [the god] rolled.
[The god] extracted from her [Earth], her water and her greenery.
And [through] the mountains he [the god] anchored her [Earth or the land].
As provisions [or bounties] for you and your livestock.

It's fairly obvious from this set of verses that Earth is what's at the center of the discussion, not mountains, so that the pronoun *her* in verse 79:32 must be referring to Earth, not to mountains. This is further supported by the set's overall communication of how the god "set Earth up" for humanity, as evident by the set's concluding statement expressed through the last verse. To achieve this goal, the god created Earth, extracted from her water (a vital substance for life), extracted her greenery (vital food), and *fixed* her (through the creation of mountains). All these can be seen as being logical prerequisites to Earth becoming useful to humanity and its livestock. To propose that what verse 79:32 is referring to as "mountains being set firmly" is outside of the overall context of the verses, and such firm setting has nothing to do with the inherent meaning of the concluding statement. Thus, instead of translating verse 79:32 as *And the mountains he [the god] set firmly*, the common translation should have translated the verse as *And the mountains he [the god] set firming*. This is more in line with the general context and overall meaning of what verses 79:30–33 are communicating.

The last point I'll make concerns verses 21:31 and 16:15. In these verses, the Quran uses the words *en tameed*, which means "to not sway," "to not shift," or "to not move,"[123] when referring to land, while also making mention of *rawaseya*. It's thus clear from these verses that the Quran associates *rawaseya* with "not swaying, shifting, or moving." This constitutes the strongest evidence that what the Quran is communicating through *rawaseya* is, in fact, an anchoring of land in motion through the creation of mountains, thus implying a direct association between the creation of mountains and the motion of land, in agreement with plate tectonics.

The Grand Canyon

I would venture to guess that the title of this section is probably going to raise a few eyebrows. The choice will nonetheless become more evident as we finish the section and hopefully come to agree that a more appropriate title could not have been chosen. And as suspected, the Grand Canyon I intend to talk about here is none other than the famous American Grand Canyon.

The Grand Canyon, located in the western region of the United States, is one of the most awe-inspiring and striking geological features of the planet. The canyon is about 280 miles (450 km) long, 18 miles (29 km) wide in some places, with a depth of almost 6000 feet (2000 m) at times. Because of how it came to be, the canyon exposes sections of Earth's crust that go as far back as 2 billion years (almost half the age of the planet itself) in a manner not readily or easily observable from anywhere else on Earth. The

---

123. Cowan, *Hans Wehr Dictionary*, 1095.

Grand Canyon was formed by a number of geological forces that included plate tectonics and erosion, but the canyon itself was literally carved by the waters of the Colorado River over millions of years, long before our own species appeared on the scene.[124] With this introduction, let's now examine the following verse:

> And surely, of the stones [or rocks] are those with rivers gushing through, and surely of them [the stones or rocks] are ones that are cut with water exiting out of them.
>
> (2:74)

Verse 2:74 uses the key words *rocks* (*hijar*: "stones"), *gushing* (from *fej'jer*: "overflow, gush out, shoot out, pour forth"), *rivers* (*enhar*), *cut* (*yesh'shuq*: "split, tear, cut open, carve"), *exiting* (*yekh'ruj*: "exiting, coming out"), and *water* (*ma'a*). Now, the powerful erosive capability of water with respect to carving stone takes place over long periods of time, normally measured in millions or tens of millions of years. It's an event that cannot be witnessed within a single person's lifetime and, in the case of the Grand Canyon, not even in the lifetime of the entire human species. It's also somewhat counterintuitive, because for a person to carve stone normally requires a hard object used with significant force. Yet, this verse exactly describes our modern scientific understanding of how a geological formation such as the Grand Canyon was created through the sheer force of water.

Formation of Crude Oil

Crude oil (or petroleum, as it's also known) is a substance that comes from deeper layers within Earth. Today, crude oil has become one of our most important raw materials, as it's the substance that the gasoline and diesel fuel we use to power our automobiles, trucks, trains, and airplanes comes from. It's also the source of many vital chemical products we've grown accustomed to using over the years, including pharmaceuticals, solvents, fertilizers, pesticides, and plastics.

Crude oil is characteristically black in color and comes to us from ancient fossilized organic material (or biomass), such as that from prehistoric trees, animals, algae, and certain plankton species that lived a few hundred million years ago and that have since died and become buried beneath various layers of sand and rock deep within Earth. Over long periods of time—millions of years—this organic matter was mixed with mud and transformed into crude oil by Earth's high levels of pressure (or squeezing)

---

124. At eight pounds per gallon, large amounts of rapidly flowing water result in a significant cutting force.

and heat deep underground.[125] The Quran has provided a set of verses that talk about this general process and about the eventual formation of crude oil as we've come to understand it:

> *[Muhammad] remember [or whisper repeatedly] your life giver's name, the highest. The one who created and made straight [or laid in order]. And the one who estimated [or calculated] and guided [or provided the way]. And the one who extracted the pastures [or greenery], and made [or turned] into a black [or blackish, dark] scum.*
>
> (87:1–5)

These verses indicate that *pastures* (*mer'a*: "pastures, grasslands") can be *made* or *turned into* (*ja'al*: "to make, render, cause to be or become") *black* (*ah'wa*: "black, dark") *scum* (*ghutha*). Let's begin by examining the word *mer'a*. *Mer'a* has traditionally been translated as grazing or grass lands because its root word, *re'a*, means "to nurture" or "to provide for," which is why *mer'a* has assumed its typical meaning, given the nourishment function grasslands provide to the herds of livestock that people relied on for their own livelihood and survival during ancient times. *Mer'a*, however, can mean other things. If we carry the root meaning of *mer'a* into a sea or ocean environment, then *mer'a* can also mean things such as plankton and algae, as well as other microscopic marine species, all of which also act as foods for larger sea creatures. These, in turn, can be transformed into crude oil if sufficient quantities are buried, pressed, and "cooked" under many layers of deposits for millions of years.

In addition to forming coal and crude oil, certain organic matter, such as plants, can turn into dark, scumlike matter known as "compost" used for enriching soil. Compost is created when plants decompose into nutrients through the action of worms, fungi, and bacteria over a period of months or years. Contrary to the creation of oil, however, composting comes about through rather simple, natural processes that do not involve the high pressures or temperatures required for oil. Composting also does not require the lengthy time frames (millions of years) normally required for oil's creation. Are verses 87:1–5 referring to something as simple as how compost comes about? Or are they referring to something as complex as the creation of coal and oil? To answer this, we need to explore the verses' choice of words and general context.

---

125. Scientists believe that crude oil came mostly from massive amounts of dead marine animal species that lived in relatively shallow seas, while coal—another energy producing substance, also black in color—came mostly from dead plants and trees.

The verses start out asking Muhammad to *seb'bih* (what I translate as "remember" or "whisper repeatedly"). *Seb'bih* is normally understood to be the act of thinking and voicing awe and amazement for something that is grand or majestic. As such, the reader of these verses would expect this word to be followed by things that are special and wondrous, which is in fact the case since the verses mention making things "straight" after the initial creation (a topic we'll explore in greater depth in the next chapter) and estimating and inspiring form and function into everything (a topic we'll explore in more depth in chapter 10). Because of this, it would be somewhat out of place for the Quran to follow these lengthy and laborious aspects of our natural world with the simple process of composting. Thus, it makes better logical sense for these verses to be referring to the processes of coal and oil production, which, in addition to coal's and oil's large benefit to humanity, are quite complex and lengthy, in line with the verses' overall theme.

Earth's Environmental Problems

It would be difficult to convince anyone that Earth today does not potentially face a set of significant environmental challenges. We've all heard of acid rain, ozone depletion, the poisoning of aquatic species in our rivers, species destruction due to increased economic activities, and global warming, among the many other dire issues our planet faces. We're also beginning to discover that Earth is a delicate planet and that our actions, as a species, are causing severe and perhaps irreversible harm to it. One scientist recently estimated that by the year 2300, the human species will have destroyed about 60 percent of all other species on planet Earth, an assessment that, if true, is sadly unthinkable. In a mere 200,000 years—the span of time our species has existed on this planet—we would have caused as much species destruction as the natural event that wiped out the dinosaurs, but which occurs, on average, only once every 100 million years! The Quran has captured our species general indifference to the health of this planet, and to life on it, through the following verse:

> *Great hurt [or difficulty] has appeared on land and in the sea through what people have done, so that he [the god] gives them [the people] a taste of what they have done, hoping they reverse their ways.*
>
> (30:41)

As far as applying the correct interpretation to this verse, there is perhaps no better time period to apply this verse to than the period following the nineteenth-century industrial revolution and the large global consumption capacities since created, which have directly caused many of Earth's environmental problems. This interpretation is clearly evident by the verse's use of *great hurt* (*fasad*: "decay, corruption, disintegration, evil"), on *land* (*berr*) and in the *sea* (*ba'har*: "sea, ocean"), *what people have done* (*keseb'et ay'di el-nas*: "what people have profited or gained from"), and *reverse* their ways (from *rej'ee*: "return, come back, revert to").

Earth's Melting Ice Caps

As stated in the previous section, Earth is facing a number of environmental problems, and one of these is global warming. Global warming (also known as climate change) is understood as the increase of near-surface and ocean temperatures due to higher levels of greenhouse gases that result from increased levels of human economic activities. Many scientists today believe that global warming is directly responsible for the continuous melting and shrinking of Earth's polar ice caps, leading perhaps to further environmental and ecological disasters for our planet down the road. I once saw a short video clip of an Alaskan native who was describing how, within his own lifetime (a period of perhaps forty or fifty years), he has witnessed tall ice glaciers continuously recede and almost disappear—an unfortunate story that's probably told by many other mystified natives. I believe that the Quran has spoken of the future melting and shrinking of Earth's polar ice caps in the following two verses:

> *Do they [humanity, the perpetrators] not see that we [the god] approach Earth and we decrease her from her edges, so are they the winners?*
>
> (21:44)

> *Do they [humanity, the perpetrators] not see that we [the god] approach Earth decreasing her from her edges, and the god judges [or decides], and no one changes that judgment [or decision], and he is quick in his accounting.*
>
> (13:41)

The key words in these verses are *Earth* (*ardh*), *decrease* (from *nuqs*: "to decrease, diminish, lessen"), and *edges* (*atraf*: "limits, extremities, edges, tips"). First, I will clarify that the interpretation I propose for these verses as pertaining to Earth's polar ice caps is not the standard interpretation. Some interpreters have proposed that Earth decreases in size with time, while others believe that these verses refer to Earth's somewhat squeezed shape. What is clear from the verses, however, is that something *unacceptable* is going on with humanity. And this unacceptable behavior, which the Quran does not specify, requires accountability, judgment, and perhaps even punishment by the god.

This interpretation may lead some readers to begin to wonder if the god of the Quran is "an angry god," as may be implied by verses 21:44 and 13:41.

I think that a direct answer to this question is somewhat irrelevant. Anger is a human emotion, and it appears in the Quran purely to serve a communicative purpose and should not be understood as representing an inherent or core quality of the god. So instead of providing a direct answer, I'll point to the important concept of Haqq I mentioned in chapters 1 and 4. As I alluded to then, we simply cannot exist or live outside of the bounds of this concept of truth, balance, or fairness any more than we can exist or live outside of the fundamental laws of nature. And when Haqq is violated, there will be consequences—at times quite severe ones—according to the Quran.

In a sense, the god, too, is also bound by Haqq, and because of this the Quran placed this concept above that of the god in several key verses. Having said this, I also think that the god of the Quran is a god that wants to see humanity happy and prosperous, as is evident by so many other verses. However, such a false or misleading sense of happiness and prosperity cannot come on Haqq's account, as I believe these verses are intending to communicate. It seems that our fate is ultimately within our own hands!

Earth's Ultimate State

The story of our beautiful blue-green planet will one day come to an end. This will happen when our sun ceases to exist in about 5 billion years, when it is estimated to run out of fuel. And when our sun dies, our planet will die along with it. As noted earlier, when our sun approaches the end of its life, it will first begin to expand to a very large size and become what's known as a red giant; in doing so, it may even engulf Earth. If the sun does not engulf Earth, it will literally fry its surface. All of Earth's oceans will evaporate; forests will burn and die; life will cease to exist; and the planet will turn into a large, very hot, and dead rock.[126] The Quran has foretold this fate for Earth in the following verses:

> We [the god] have surely made everything on Earth as [or for] her beauty, so that we see which ones are the most virtuous

---

126. Another possible scenario for how life might become extinct on Earth in several billion years, according to scientists, is if Earth's interior cools so much that its molten iron core freezes, thus eliminating Earth's magnetic shield and exposing the planet to deadly solar wind radiation, similar to what happened on Mars.

[referring to humanity]. And we are surely turning everything on her [Earth] into a barren [or lifeless] plateau [or plain].
(18:7–8)

The important words in these verses are *ardh*, *beauty* (*zeena*: "ornament, adornment, beauty"), *most virtuous* (*ah'senu amala*: "best laborers, excellent performers"), *barren* (*ju'ruza*), and *plateau* (*sa'eed*: "level, plain, plateau").

It's sometimes worth reflecting on how temporary and passing things really are, even for the grandest of things. I can't help at times but think about how Earth was once a large, inhospitable, and smoldering piece of rock, and it will again return to being a large, inhospitable, and smoldering piece of rock. But somewhere in between, perhaps right about now, Earth is a beautiful, inspiring, and truly unique place.

7 Life's Origin and Evolution

The time has come for us to focus on one of the most intriguing and beautiful aspects of our universe: life. The topics that concern the nature of life and what precisely *defines* life are still somewhat elusive within the realm of science. It seems that scientists can easily point out what is alive from what is not, but coming up with an all-encompassing construct or definition that clearly delineates the boundary of life is more challenging. Nevertheless, life constitutes a wonderful mark of our universe in general and of our planet in particular, as manifested by the astonishing degree of beauty and diversity within the realm of life, as well as by the sheer power of the force that is life.

In this chapter, I describe the Quran's account of how life originated, how it evolved, how man came to be, and the importance of water to the very notion of life. As I've done thus far, I'll start with the science, follow with verses of the Quran, and conclude with a discussion of the agreement between the two. Let's begin by briefly reviewing the current scientific account of life's origin and evolution. Although many details of this account are yet to be filled in, scientists are in overwhelming agreement as to the basic principles and general processes that govern life on our planet.

Much of what scientists know about the nature and progression of life on Earth is based on extensive studies of fossil records, detailed anatomical studies of various species, and advanced DNA research and analysis. All of this knowledge, which was arguably nonexistent until only recently in human history, points to a rather important conclusion: life *evolved* on planet Earth. How exactly did life originate? When did it originate? Where did it originate? And how did it progress since that time? These are some of the key questions that concern the mystery of life, which I'll address through established science in the next thirty or so pages of the book. Let's begin by talking about the *when*.

The exact date when life originated on Earth is not known with any certainty, but it's generally accepted by scientists today that the first life-forms appeared around 3.8 billion years ago, or even as early as 4 billion years ago—approximately 500 to 700 million years after Earth's accretion. There also seems to be general agreement that life most likely arose only once and that the first life-form was quite simple compared to later multi-cellular organisms. What's much lesser certain than the *when*, however, are the *where* and the *how*.

Leading scientists have put forward several theories over the years to shed more light on the *where* and *how*, but none of these theories have presented the conclusive evidence needed to confirm it to be *the* account of the origin of life. One of the major challenges that scientists face is that even though this first life was quite primitive, it was at the same time quite complex and next to impossible to synthesize in any laboratory environment. Because of this, scientists believe that it must have taken an ingenious and elaborate process under very special circumstances to successfully assemble the first molecules of life as well as assemble the complex follow-on systems that perform vital life functions. The molecules of life include lipids (or fats), carbohydrates, proteins, and nucleic acids, while the systems of life include things such as cell membranes and centers for energy production known as mitochondria, in addition to the whole cells that comprise the true building blocks of advanced multicellular life.[127] In addition to the successful creation of life-enabling molecules and complex systems, all of early life's systems and system components had to successfully work together in the face of a hostile and dynamic external environment.

Given all these challenges and delicate interdependencies that life first faced, it's understandable why scientists have been unable to synthesize any form of organic life, including simple ones, despite the many sincere (and quite advanced) efforts to do so. In many important respects, the famous phrase "the miracle of life" is probably not an exaggeration in the least—we really are *very fortunate* to be here.

To further drive home this point, a particular scientific school of thought is now advancing the notion that, although primitive life may be common in the universe, the existence of highly advanced forms of life, such as that of our own, is exceedingly rare. It's thus very likely that our planet is the only home to intelligent life in the galaxy, perhaps even within the larger universe. In spite of this, scientists are not discounting the possibility that intelligent life may arise in the future (or the present) on or within many places in this unbelievably vast universe. Such optimism was succinctly captured by a NASA scientist who once stated that the universe can be thought of as being "pregnant" with life.

With this brief introduction to the challenges of life's early emergence,

---

127. It's really difficult for most of us to truly comprehend and appreciate the realm of cells, with their overwhelming degree of organization, efficiency, and mind-boggling complexity, all packed into a size that cannot even be seen by the naked eye.

let's now begin to examine the Quran's account of life's origin and evolution. But before we do, let's endeavor to better appreciate the importance of liquid water to the very notion of life, as well as examine the Quran's account in this regard.

Water's Vital Role

Liquid water's crucially important role in the emergence of life on planet Earth cannot be overstated. Carbon-based organic life, the type of life on Earth, simply could not have emerged without the existence of liquid water. In many respects, as far as planet Earth is concerned, water *is* life.

Because water is especially effective at dissolving other compounds (which is why it's sometimes referred to as the universal solvent), water is the primary medium through which vital life-related biochemical reactions take place. In addition, water constitutes a key component of many of life's crucial metabolic processes, including those of respiration and photosynthesis.[128] Furthermore, cells, the basic building blocks of multicellular life-forms, are themselves mostly composed of water and are the reason why we humans are two-thirds water by weight.

The water molecule, which contains two hydrogen atoms and one oxygen atom, is a special molecule that possesses rather interesting properties, some of which have enabled water to protect life on Earth. For instance, contrary to the behavior of other molecules, water molecules become less dense (and lighter) when they freeze. This enabled the oceans' lighter ice to float on top of the heavier liquid water when Earth was believed to have completely frozen during what's been called "snowball Earth," periods our planet experienced more than once throughout its 4.5-billion-year history. This shielding has in turn allowed water in the oceans to remain in the liquid state for very long periods of time—a fortunate outcome that ended up preserving their various life-forms.[129]

Water is also special in that the amount of energy that must be added to change its state from liquid into gas, or the amount of energy that must be extracted to change its state from liquid into solid, are among the highest of any known substance. This special property has in turn helped moderate Earth's surface temperature as water evaporates and freezes. Also, water possesses a high specific heat property, meaning that the amount of energy required to raise a unit mass of water by one degree Celsius is relatively high. As such, water maintains relatively steady temperatures during extended

---

128. Metabolism is the means by which a living organism extracts energy from food as well as the means by which cell components are produced and maintained.

129. Water is unique in that it is the only natural substance that can exist in all of its possible states (gas, liquid, and solid) on Earth's surface.

periods of planetary heating and cooling, which further helps stabilize global temperatures on very long time scales. Because of water's high specific heat, the oceans have been dubbed "Earth's natural thermostat," and humans—being two-thirds water—would not survive a summer, or even a mild winter, in the absence of this vital insulating property.

Another important aspect of water is how it relates to plate tectonics, the process we learned about in chapter 6. Many scientists believe that the process of plate tectonics—itself vitally important to many aspects of Earth's ability to support complex life—is dependent on the availability of an abundant amount of surface liquid water. Scientists also believe that the salty oceans of the Earth, not fresh water or land, are what constituted the true cradle of animal life for our planet. These salty waters are believed to have spawned every animal phylum and every basic body plan that exists today or that has ever existed on our planet. Water's benefit to living organisms goes even deeper, since water also possesses a very high "surface tension" property, which allows vital nutrients to be transported easily through structures such as roots and veins. I should also point out that although water was crucial to the early emergence of life, equally important was having an abundant amount of liquid water—which also appears to be "just the right amount" for Earth—so that life could continue to evolve into more complex forms.

These overall benefits of water, along with its importance to life in general, are probably best summarized by a scientist who, while discussing his efforts with NASA to locate life elsewhere in the universe, once remarked, "Show me a planet with liquid water, and I'll show you a planet that can harbor life."[130]

Water's importance to life has been captured by the Quran through the following verses:

> *Do the ones who deny [the existence of the god] not see that the skies and Earth [or the land] were one and we [the god] separated them, and from water we brought life to every living thing [or from water we gave life to everything]? Do they not believe?*
>
> (21:30)

> *And the god created every mover from water, so that some move on their stomachs, and some move on two legs, and some*

---

130. Water is so important to life on Earth that every living life-form, including the simplest form of life (bacteria), requires water for its survival.

*move on four legs. He [the god] creates what he wills. The god
is surely completely capable of anything.*

(24:45)

*And he [the god] is the one who created people from water, and
made them related, and your [Muhammad's] life giver has
always been very capable.*

(25:54)

Since the first verse mentions water immediately following the separation of Earth and sky, it's most likely describing the planet's early environment shortly after it formed. You may recall from chapter 6 that as Earth cooled, degassing caused various gases to fill the early atmosphere, which upon further cooling condensed to form liquid water (rain) and the first oceans some 4.3 billion years ago. The second verse is most likely describing the evolution of life from Earth's oceans, in agreement with our current scientific understanding of how fish evolved into amphibians, amphibians evolved into reptiles, and reptiles evolved into mammals—a process that started about 600 million years ago. It's also interesting to note that the second verse may be referring to various "body plans" and that all of these body plans have originated from water in agreement with scientific belief. Water as the birthplace for complex life is further confirmed by the third verse, which states that humans originated from water.

There is an important point to be made here with respect to the god's capability, explicitly called out in the second and third verses. Clearly, these verses are trying to communicate an elaborate or difficult process going on and one that requires this capability so that the life-forms mentioned in the verses can spring forth from water. I believe that this elaborate or difficult process is a direct reference to evolution, a theory we'll discuss in greater detail later in the chapter.

The First Living Ancestor

Just as linguists have established that all human languages come from a common origin, scientists believe that all life may have a common origin as well. This common origin is called the *last universal common ancestor*, or LUCA. LUCA is thought to be the very first life-form, or, more likely, closely related (in time) to the first life-form, which evolved some 4 billion years ago and from which *all* subsequent life on Earth came to be.

If you want to understand how all of Earth's life-forms are related to each other and if you want to capture that understanding in a picture (since it's worth a thousand words, as the old adage goes), you come up with a simple and familiar depiction: a tree. The branches of this tree represent the different life species that live on Earth today or that have ever lived.[131] And just as the branches of a typical tree subdivide into other branches, species, too, "subdivide" into other species through a process known as evolution. This "tree of life" has been drawn by scientists and was found to confirm that each of Earth's species falls into one of three domains, with each domain representing something like a smaller tree within the larger tree of life. These three domains are called *archaea*, *bacteria*, and *eukarya*. This classification scheme has been well supported through extensive DNA analysis of many different species and has been unanimously accepted by the wider scientific community since first proposed in the latter part of the twentieth century.

Our ancestor, LUCA, also belongs to the tree of life and is located, as you might suspect, at its base, near where the trunk meets the ground (imagine the tree of life as a tree without roots). Also, since no single species can live forever and eventually becomes extinct, the branches of the tree of life also eventually become "pruned," depicting the extinction of a particular species. As I stated earlier, no one knows where, or exactly how long ago, LUCA lived, but the evidence pointing to it as the origin of all subsequent life on Earth is compelling. This evidence comes from the discovery of the genetic code (or DNA) in the early 1950s and the subsequent confirmation that this genetic code is common to all life on Earth, an understanding that is supported by a great many discoveries. For instance, more than 99 percent of human genes (a gene is a small portion of the genetic code) have a related counterpart in a mouse, and despite more than 500 million years of evolutionary separation, half of the genes in the sea squirt correspond to ones humans have too. Further illustrating this genetic commonality, a particular gene taken from a human being can be "read" (or processed) by the "translation machinery" (or processing facility) of a bacterium. In another stunning experiment, researchers recently identified the gene responsible for the luminosity of a certain species of jellyfish. Scientists then extracted that gene and surgically planted it into a mouse, which also became luminous following the transplant.

It's also well established that all life on Earth shares a set of key commonalties: all life is composed of cells, all life has genes made of DNA, and all life shares the method (or code) by which proteins are made from the combination of various amino acids (the building blocks of proteins). In addition, all life today shares a common core of metabolic reactions (remember that metabolism is one of the most important processes of life), at the heart of which is an all-important reaction (or "metabolic pathway") called the Krebs cycle.

---

131. A species is a collection of members who only interbreed among themselves.

Yet another remarkable example that clearly illustrates how all life is closely related is in the commonality of essential structures found in various forms of life. As I'll describe in a little more detail, genes are the heredity units of living organisms that contain instructions for "what to do," similar to how a set of instructions tells you how to assemble a piece of furniture from its component parts.[132] Not all genes are equally important, though, and there appears to be a hierarchy of sorts when it comes to gene functions. Among some of the more important of these genes are the so-called "Hox genes," which is short for *homeobox*. Hox genes, which play a vital role in the formation of body-axis patterning in all known animals, contain the special gene domains known as the homeodomains. The most interesting aspect of these homeodomains, scientists came to discover, is that they are *shared* among animal and plant forms of life (including, of course, humans). Because of their functional importance and this peculiar commonality, homeodomains are thought by scientists to be conserved (passed on from one form of life to another) through billions of years of time. A telling example of this is that the head, eye, mouth, gut, limbs, and many other systems of an insect bear general and genetic continuity with human versions of the same, which we even share with shellfish.

All of these life commonalities, along with many more similar examples, constitute without any doubt a key piece of evidence in establishing that there was a LUCA and that this LUCA originated all life on Earth through evolution. Indeed, evolutionary theory has shown life's connectedness in overwhelming detail and beyond any doubt.

In this section of the chapter, I illustrate how there are multiple references to LUCA within the Quran. My proposed interpretation of the respective verses of the Quran is contrary to that of the standard interpretation, which in my view is scientifically unacceptable and must therefore be discarded in light of recent scientific discovery and knowledge. Let's now examine these references:

[The god] created you [humanity] from one life and then later made from her [the one life], her mate.[133]

(39:6)

Humanity: Be thoughtful [or very aware] of your life giver, who

---

132. Unlike the instructions of DNA, however, furniture assembly instructions always seem to be missing one or two key steps, making for a frustrating evening filled with colorful language!

133. The pronoun *her* is used because *nefs*, the Arabic word for "life," is of the female form.

created you from one life, and created from this life her mate,
and sprung forth from the two many men and women.

(4:1)

And he [the god] is the one who established you [humanity]
from one life and into a stable [or steady, settled] repository
[or depot]. We have surely explained the verses [or signs] for a
thoughtful [or comprehending] people.

(6:98)

He [the god] is the one who created you [humanity] from one
life, and made from her, her mate, so that he [the mate] finds
calmness [or attraction] with her [the one life].

(7:189)

As far as these verses go, the standard interpretation points unanimously to the one life as that of *Adem* (the biblical Adam) and the mate as that of *Ha'wa* (the biblical Eve). While I do not dispute the existence of Adam and Eve at some point in our ancestry, I believe these verses are describing LUCA, the common ancestor to all life we just learned about. Let's take a closer look at these verses, focusing special attention on the second and third ones.

In the second verse, the god is asking humanity to be thoughtful or very aware of, as in fearful of, the god.[134] When the Quran wants to draw such attention, it normally provides some sort of substantiation. Here, this substantiation comes in the form of explaining how we have all sprung forth from this one life and how this one life, along with its mate, generated all of humanity. On the surface, it may appear that the verse is pointing to Adam and Eve, but "on the surface" doesn't always work with the Quran, as noted throughout the book. Let's ponder a few important points.

This verse was revealed more than fourteen hundred years ago, many hundreds or thousands of generations of humans after the existence of Adam and Eve. The verse reveals nothing new or surprising by stating that many men and women came from Adam and Eve. Had the verse been revealed at a time shortly after Adam and Eve lived, when only a handful of modern humans existed, then we could have said that the verse revealed something telling and worthy of paying attention to—the creation of a great multitude of humans at some point in the future from just two

---

134. The verse should not be understood as alluding to a god who seeks to needlessly strike fear into the hearts of his subjects but, instead, understood as the god's communication that he will hold all accountable in accordance with Haqq.

individuals. Telling us recently that many men and women came from Adam and Eve is not attention grabbing in the least. The natural response would be why must I or anyone else be fearful or cognizant of this god following an outcome that is completely within the realm of the ordinary? The verse thus does not substantiate the need to be thoughtful of the god. On the other hand, this picture is turned completely upside down (or, more appropriately, right side up) if the first life is not that of a full-blown human but of a mere speck of life. Now I'm paying attention! This is a god that can spring forth an entire human collective—along with civilizations capable of much influence and creativity—from a simple and seemingly insignificant form of life. The verse thus accomplishes this substantiation very well now, and when this god speaks, I listen.

Let's next turn our attention to the third verse. There are two words in this verse that the standard interpretation does not explain: *stable* (*musta'qar*: "stable, settled, firm, unchanging, site, location, place") and *repository* (*mustow'da*: "repository, storage, depot"). The verse simply does not make sense if we interpret the *one life* (*nef'sin wa'hida*: "one life, one person, one soul, or one essence") as that of Adam. And in such a case, what exactly is this stable repository? It was actually this verse that drove me to interpret the one life as that of LUCA, as I became convinced that these words were referring to the evolution of species from simpler life-forms in accordance with evolution.

Today we understand that when a new species evolves it maintains a distinct and stable (or unchanging) identity through its unique DNA code (or genetic pool) and through reproduction only with members of its own species. The species' DNA thus becomes "an unchanging place of storage" distinct from that of any other species (to a large extent; there's always slight individual variability). The verse furthermore seems to imply that there will be confusion to its true meaning but that a clear explanation has been provided for people who are thoughtful and wish to understand.

When I first suspected that *stable repository* was describing how species evolve, I decided to search the Quran for any other verses that may contain these words, hoping that these newfound meanings would further confirm what I suspected. This ability of the Quran to "explain itself" at times—a concept first taught by the prophet Muhammad—has been well accepted within Quranic scholarly circles ever since the Quran was first revealed. Sure enough, I discovered another verse that contained the same exact two words and in the same order as this verse. It was as if the Quran was pointing to this new verse and asking the reader to infer the correct meaning of *stable repository* from it. When I looked at this new verse I became completely convinced that these words were talking about the evolution of species. Here's the new verse:

And there is not a single mover in Earth [or the land] except
that the god ensures her sustenance [or livelihood] and he [the
god] knows her stable repository, all of which is in a clear book.
(11:6)

Clearly, this verse is talking to the great variety of living things on and in Earth (the plural of *mover* is *dawab*: "animals") and how their dietary needs (*rizq*: "livelihood, nourishment, subsistence") are "on the god's mind." The fact that the verse associated a great variety of life-forms on Earth with *stable repository* is itself quite telling, but then the verse associates these two words with a *book* (*kitab*), which I'll go over in more detail later in the chapter.[135] With this newfound knowledge, we can now see a new reading of verse 11:6 that is logical and scientifically accurate: *And there is not a single mover in Earth [or the land] except that the god ensures her sustenance [or livelihood], and he [the god] knows her species type [or identity] and this species type [or identity] is in [or is defined by] the genetic code of that species.*

Interestingly, verse 6:98 is also located in the chapter of "The Animals," which constitutes another clue in our story—the significance of the location of a particular verse within the Quran—that we'll revisit later. Returning to verse 6:98, we can reasonably conclude that *stable repository* refers to our species type (the modern human genetic pool) and that *one life* represents LUCA, not Adam.[136]

Let's now turn our attention to verses 39:6 and 7:189. These verses talk to how there was *one life* first, and then at a later time its *mate* (*zawj*: "spouse, mate") was created from it so that there could be attraction and harmony (or a "seeking") between the two (*yes'kun*: "become calm, tranquil, or peaceful with"). Before explaining these verses, however, I need to provide some background as to why the standard interpretation provides the mistaken interpretation that it does and why such interpretation has become so influenced. So let's next briefly talk about the foundations of the Islamic faith.

The Islamic religion is primarily based on two foundations.[137] The first of these is the Quran, and the second is "the way of the prophet." The way of the prophet is captured in the way the prophet Muhammad lived his life and conducted (or helped conduct) the affairs of Muslims over a twenty-

---

135. *Kitab* refers to the genetic code.

136. Additionally, verse 6:98 uses the key word *established*, which, as I note throughout, is meant to signify a highly elaborate undertaking. If the one life signifies Adam, then it would not make sense for verse 6:98 to use *established*.

137. These foundations should not to be confused with the "pillars" mentioned in chapter 1.

three-year period. A major part of this tradition is what we've learned as the *prophetic sayings*, given in chapter 2, which constitute what the prophet was confirmed to have said in matters of importance. These sayings are sacred in a sense because Muslims believe that the prophet, any prophet, is ultimately guided through the divine. In other words, a prophet lives his life in a way that reflects how the god wants to see others live, or try to live, their lives.

While this may sound quite reasonable, the problem is (and no Muslim has ever disputed this) that unlike the Quran, the prophetic sayings are not subject to any "godly preservation." This means that any particular prophetic saying within our possession today may or may not have come from the prophet Muhammad. What is well accepted today is that following the death of the prophet, Muslim scholars developed ways of cross-checking, as well as other means of ascertaining whether a particular saying originated from the prophet. However, such mechanisms were subject to heavy, and at times extremely corrupt, political influences that have caused some to "cast doubt on" a small fraction of the sayings that have even "passed the test." This is further complicated by the (also indisputable) fact that the prophet himself foretold of some Muslims creating false "sayings" following his death in order to advance certain interests, or they may even be the result of well-meaning clumsiness and error. Many of these sayings have been later discovered and put into doubt, while others have remained part of the Islamic tradition to this day.

One of these sayings has to do with the prophet Muhammad claiming that Eve was created from Adam's rib and as a "first creation." They (those speaking falsely on behalf of the prophet) even go on to attribute more related false sayings, such as the prophet saying, "Because Eve was created from a rib, do not try to bend it too much (as in cause emotional abuse), otherwise you might break it" (as in causing irreversible marital damage).

You would think, given the numerous creation verses in the Quran and the sheer importance of this event, that the Quran would contain an account of Adam being the one life and Eve coming from his rib. But such an account is clearly absent from the Quran. The Quran could have also easily substituted *one life* with *Adam* if this was indeed the case. Fortunately in this case, however, we now know that this same account is also reported within the Judeo-Christian tradition. This means that Muhammad, having lived six hundred years after Jesus, could not possibly have been the originator of this account. I suspect that this account may even predate the Judeo-Christian era, given its "typical myth" sound. Many such myths were known to ancient cultures throughout the world, including the general area of the present-day Middle East. Notwithstanding this, however, the belief that Eve was created from Adam's rib is still the accepted viewpoint within common Islamic tradition and has greatly shaped the standard interpretation of the one life as referring to Adam. Later in this chapter, I will touch on a suite of Quranic verses that pertain to Adam being "cast out of paradise" and angels being asked to "prostrate to Adam," all of which seem on the surface to strengthen the currently accepted view that Adam was the one life created "instantaneously." During that discussion, I will challenge the standard interpretation for those verses as well and offer an alternate interpretation that emphasizes the one life as not referring to Adam. This will offer a consistent Quranic account of the creation of humanity, one that is in agreement with established modern science.

This is also an appropriate place to make an important point. There is an Islamic school of thought that argues that the Quran will never be completely understood, and so there is no point in trying to explain the many verses that seem to be unclear or difficult to understand. Many of these verses fall within the realm of the science of the Quran, while others are simply too vague or lie outside of humanity's domain of knowledge (I refer to these as "gray verses"[138]). While I sympathize with this general concern, I do not subscribe to the perspective that the Quran should be "left alone." In addition to such a perspective leading to and fostering a general environment of ignorance and blind following—a dangerous perspective, in my view—it goes against the essence of the Quran in urging and encouraging the acts of thinking, exploring, and discovering. However, I do accept that our human knowledge is ultimately quite limited and that some of the gray verses cannot be interpreted through our limited set of cognitive and linguistic resources (but I also hold firm that even these verses hold deeper meanings that ultimately can and will be understood).

Let's resume our discussion on the first and fourth verses. What can they mean if the one life does not refer to Adam? Who or what is the mate? And what does finding calmness between the two mean?

Current scientific theory tells us that the first life on Earth did not reproduce through sexual means (with a partner) but that this capability evolved at a later time. We also know today that all humans, animals, and plants evolved from an ancestor that reproduced through sexual means and has been identified as a single-celled eukaryotic species (recall the three domains of life). Some scientists have also proposed that the more complex eukaryotic cell evolved only once and arose only when two much simpler prokaryotic cells (prokaryotic cells include the archaea [single-celled microorganisms] and bacteria domains and do not reproduce sexually) found each other, against all odds, and became united in what has been called the

---

138. The gray verses that deal with topics at hand are 2:30–37, 7:11–27, 15:28–42, 17:61–65, 20:115–126, and 38:71–83.

"fateful encounter" hypothesis. Thus, I believe that this later evolution of sexual reproduction is what the Quran is most likely describing in these verses. The fourth verse describes how the two lives needed to "seek each other" as previously noted, clearly pointing to a sexually reproductive environment. The first verse also talks about how this took place "then later" (*thum'ma*: "then, later on, after that") from when the one (first) life came to be, which agrees with the scientific understanding of the development of complex life.

The Origin of Humanity

What is the Quran's view on the origin of humanity? I'll attempt to answer this question in this section while presenting and explaining the verses that pertain to how modern human beings came to be. Let's begin by examining these verses:

> Humanity: If you are in doubt about the resurrection, then we [the god] created you from clay particles [or powder, dust, sediment].
>
> (22:5)

> From her [Earth] we [the god] created you [humanity], and into her we will return you, and from her we will extract you yet again.
>
> (20:55)

> And as we [the god] told the angels: Prostrate to Adam, and they prostrated, except Iblees [the biblical Satan], who answered: Do I prostrate to what you [the god] created from wet clay [or soil, mud]?
>
> (17:61)

> And we [the god] surely created man from clay [or soil, mud] from sharpened [or pointed, teethed] clay.
>
> (15:26)

> [The god] created man from clay [or mud, soil] like earthenware [or pottery].
>
> (55:14)

> And of his [the god] signs is that he created you [humanity] from clay particles [or powder, dust, sediment], and then later you are people spreading about.
>
> (30:20)

The one [the god] who made beautiful [or fine] everything he created, and started [or began] man's [or humanity's] creation from wet clay [or soil, mud].

(32:7)

We [the god] surely created them [humanity] from a sticking [or adhering] form of wet clay [or soil, mud].

(37:11)

He [the god] is most knowledgeable about you [humanity] as he established you from Earth [or the land].

(53:32)

He [the god] established you [humanity] from Earth [or the land].

(11:61)

Before we continue with our discussion of these verses, I'll need to briefly touch on the accepted Islamic viewpoint of the creation of humanity that's supported by the standard interpretation of the Quran. This interpretation assumes that the god somehow, mysteriously, grabbed a handful of clay, molded it into the shape of Adam, and blew into it (this particular blowing will be addressed in more detail later), resulting in Adam coming to life. The process the standard interpretation envisions is very much like how a pottery maker produces a piece of pottery by shaping and cooking clay. Again, a quick surface read of these verses does not lead to believing otherwise, especially in the absence of any convincing alternative explanation. Yet, a convincing alternative explanation is what I propose. But before I do, we'll need to revisit the scientific account of how life arose on Earth almost 4 billion years ago.

As I mentioned earlier in the chapter, no one knows exactly how or where Earth's first life came to be, but several plausible theories have thus far been advanced. One of these theories, called the clay origin of life, proposes a process that may be strikingly similar to the Quran's account of how life arose.[139] This theory was first proposed by the Scottish scientist Alexander Graham Cairns-Smith (born 1931) in the latter part of the twentieth century, the details of which he captured in his book, *Seven Clues to the Origin of Life*. In his book, he describes how carbon-based life on Earth

---

139. None of the theories that attempt to describe how life originated on Earth today can be considered established science, but they provide plausible explanations for how life might have arisen.

could have originated from inorganic, "lifeless" ingredients, and he does a nice job of taking the reader through the challenges of life's creation and convincingly substantiates his claims. Cairns-Smith promotes the notion that complex organic life could not have arisen as "first life" due to the significant effort and the vast complexities associated with even the simplest forms of organic life. Instead, he suggests that organic life arose through inorganic means, specifically through a special kind of inorganic matter known as clay crystals.

Clay is known to be one of the most abundant mineral types on Earth.[140] Clay crystals can also "grow" and "reproduce" certain crystal patterns as well as certain anomalies and irregularities. These patterns and irregularities can then be used as a storage medium for vast amounts of "information" necessary for life to reproduce and evolve. Cairns-Smith believes that the clay crystal's ability to self-reproduce or replicate, as well as its ability to house large amounts of information in the form of specific crystal attributes and then pass that information to future generations, was the mechanism that preceded the current inheritance process that's based on DNA. Cairns-Smith proposes a process called "genetic takeover," whereby organic matter buried and concentrated within clay crystal layers takes over and becomes the new form of life, which is vastly more suited than inorganic clay to evolve into beings of higher complexity.

Cairns-Smith supports his theory with a powerful example of how to build a stone archway. You may know (I didn't) that it's impossible to build a stone archway without first constructing a supporting structure such as scaffolding. To construct the archway, you must first construct the scaffolding, build the archway on top of the scaffolding, wait for the archway to settle and solidify, and end the process by removing the scaffolding, thus leaving behind a solid and functional archway. In a similar vein, organic life—even single-celled organic life—is far too delicate and complex (Cairns-Smith does an impressive job of explaining this delicacy and complexity) to have arisen directly from the environment without its own supporting structure, which, according to Cairns, was in the form of clay and clay crystals.

If we reexamine the Quranic verses in this new light, we can perceive a different interpretation emerging that challenges the mistaken standard interpretation with respect to the origin of man. Specifically, let's start by focusing on the sixth, seventh, ninth, and tenth verses. The sixth verse talks about a time lapse between the first creation and the rise of humanity,

---

140. Minerals are constituents of rocks, and rocks are made up of many different types of minerals, with each mineral possessing certain chemical and physical properties.

while the seventh verse even mentions the word *started* or *began* (*bed'a*: "to begin, start, commence, initiate"). Of course, it's well accepted that anything that has a start also possesses other points or milestones such as "middle" and "end," all of which mark the particular *process* at hand. If the creation of man was instantaneous, as the standard interpretation calls for, then it would not make sense for the Quran to use *started*. The seventh verse also mentions the word *beautiful* or *fine* (*ah'sena*: "to do well, right, excellently, or expertly") when describing the end result of this process. What this verse clearly implies is that this creation was an elaborate process "engineered" by the god and thus worthy of describing as *fine* or *beautiful*. This theme of an elaborate undertaking is plainly echoed in the ninth and tenth verses as well. These verses use the key word *established* (*insha'a*)—which within the Quran maintains a very specific meaning, one that implies an elaborate undertaking as initially noted in the previous chapter and as I'll further explain in chapter 9. Furthermore, the ninth and tenth verses clearly point to the fact that man came *from Earth* (*minn el-ardh*) through such a method. Finally, verse 25:54, which we previewed earlier in the chapter, obviously states that people (*besher*: "man, human beings") came from water (*ma'a*).

In addition to the clay theory of life, another similarly credible account of how life might have arisen on our planet advances the possibility that LUCA may have originated from the oceans, specifically from chemically active sites on the ocean floor called black and white smokers (black smokers are normally found in hot and acidic environments, while white smokers exist in milder areas).[141] I wanted to note this because I also believe that the Quran has alluded to this possibility through these particular verses:

> *Let man see [or examine] from what he was created. He was created from gushing water that exits from between the sulb and the tera'ib.*
>
> (86:5–7)

Before going any further, let me first say here that it's not my intention to make matters any muddier (no pun intended) than they need be by citing yet another account for life's origin that may or may not agree with the clay theory for life. I'm also not trying to "cover my bases" by enlisting more than one theory and proclaiming agreement between science and the Quran in this regard. As I stated earlier, scientists simply do not know, based on established science, how life arose nearly 4 billion years ago. We also do not know what phase of life's evolution the various verses of the Quran are referring to. What I am trying to do, however, is explore potential

---

141. Di Giulio, "Universal Ancestor."

agreement between science and the Quran in this area that refutes the current standard interpretation of an instantaneous creation of man. After all, the most important point I want you to walk away with from this chapter is not necessarily the Quran's telling of *how* life began but that life—according to the Quran—did indeed evolve, and the verses I've presented thus far and the ones I will present in the next section all point exactly to such a conclusion. With this said, let's begin to explore these particular verses, starting with what the standard interpretation has to say about them.

There seems to be universal agreement among Muslim scholars who follow the standard interpretation that this verse refers to the sexual coming together of a man and a woman. The root for the word *sulb* means something hard, or something that has hardened, while the word *tera'ib* has been translated to mean "female chest bones." Thus, the standard interpretation promotes the scientifically incorrect notion that a human embryo is conceived from liquid that comes from the male sexual organs (or backbone area) and the female chest bones. But can anyone fault this interpretation, given that it was put forth prior to any meaningful scientific advancement? And if we discard this interpretation, then what can these verses really mean?

In my view, these verses are referring to the hydrothermal environments of the oceans described earlier. These environments produce hydrothermal structures made from various mineral deposits that result from chemical reactions taking place in the highly active thermodynamic environment that sits between the cool waters of the ocean and the hot deep layers of Earth. Scientists also believe that these environments were widespread during Earth's early history, the time in which first life came to be.

Let's examine the words contained within these verses.

First, although the word *man* (*in'san*: "man, human being") can refer to both an individual and a species, the verses here are most likely referring to man as a species and asking that we examine how we, as a species, came about. Next, the verses specifically use the word *water* (*ma'a*), not "like water." Furthermore, this water is gushing water (*dafiq*: "gushing, jetting, bursting forth") and water that comes from *between* (*bain*) two things. The first of these is a hard or hardened thing (*sulb*), and the second is *tera'ib*. Well, the hard or hardened thing can be easily interpreted as Earth's crust, initially described in chapter 6 as Earth's outermost layer. This crust solidified, naturally hardening in the process, following the cooling of Earth from its immensely hot state shortly after it formed almost 4.6 billion years ago.

The meaning of *tera'ib*, however, is not as straightforward. If you wanted to discover the meaning of this word through a dictionary today, you either do not find a meaning or you find a meaning that points back to "female chest bones" (*tera'ib* is the plural of *tariba*: "female chest bone"). Curiously, however, the expressive form for *tera'ib* has also been commonly used to denote things that "stack on top of each other."[142] In addition, *tera'ib* bears very close resemblance to the Arabic word for sand or sediment (*turab*: "earth, dust, dirt, soil, ground"). Interpreting *tera'ib* as the plural of sand or sediment is actually quite revealing because the top layer of the ocean floor does in fact consist of various layers of sediment, and the hydrothermal environments are characterized by water that gushes out from between Earth's crust (after these waters percolate down from above and become heated and charged with various minerals and gases) and the ocean floor, which, as just noted, is characterized by various layers of sediments that come from within and outside the oceans.[143]

I will further add that verses 15:26 and 55:14 can be interpreted to offer a sort of pictorial depiction in that the clays referenced in the verses come from places that are "pointy" (*mesnoon*: "sharpened, honed, pointed") and "look like earthenware" (*fakhar*: "pottery, earthenware, crockery"). This similarity is important in my view because the structures created by hydrothermal environments have been commonly described as chimney-like. If we can accept that *tera'ib* refers to the layered sedimentary nature of the ocean floor, then the use of *turab* (clay particles) in other verses makes good sense since, as I alluded to earlier, the plural of these special types of clays can be thought of as *tera'ib*—the clear and obvious implication being that the Quran has all along been referring to a sea-floor hydrothermal environment when describing the origin of humanity.

The resemblance between what verses 86:5–7 describe and a typical "smoker" is quite striking, but this interpretation is even further supported by where these verses are located in the Quran. These verses can be found in a rather short chapter, containing only six lines and seventeen verses, and just a few verses away in the same chapter is the verse we first met in the Plate Tectonics and Mountain Formation section of chapter 6, which reads: *And [I, the god, swear] by Earth of the cracks [or faults]*. In that discussion, I explained how *cracks* should be interpreted as what separates Earth's plates, and it's precisely because of these cracks (specifically, plates moving away from each other due to thermal convection) that the hydrothermal

---

142. An example is the word *tera'iq* (Arabic for ways, paths, or roads), which is also used by the Quran to denote a stacking (see verse 23:17 in chapter 5).

143. Arabic is a language that possesses a highly complex and unusual morphology (how different words derive from a single root). For example, from the root word *keteb* (write) come the Arabic words for written, writer, author, letter, booklet, book, library, correspondence, desk, and office. Thus, proposing that *tera'ib* can, in a particular context, mean "stacked layers of sand" is not that farfetched, given its resemblance to *turab* and the expressive form typically used for stacking (*tera'ib* [female chest bones], *tera'iq*, etc.).

environments we're discussing here form in the first place (although the black smokers are usually located closer to the *cracks* than the white ones).

Finally, verses 11:61 and 53:32 hold special significance and probably constitute the strongest evidence for the Quran's agreement with established science as far as the origin of humanity is concerned. These verses clearly state that humans came "from Earth," in agreement with established science—regardless of which origin-of-life account scientists eventually confirm and regardless of which phase of human evolution the various verses of the Quran refer to. Furthermore, the verses use the word *established*, which, as I state throughout the book, is meant to convey an elaborate process taking place, as man was transformed from a humble beginning to his current highly evolved state. Thus, verses 11:61 and 53:32 confirm the science-based notion of humanity coming from a simple "Earthly" life and not through any other miraculous means.

Evolution

Generally speaking, the subject of evolution is considered taboo within the majority of Islamic circles today. This predisposition originates, in my opinion, from the false perception that the god created Adam "perfect" and that Adam was the first human to walk Earth, a perception that is well entrenched within the standard interpretation of the relevant verses of the Quran and one I intend to challenge and refute.

Many Muslim scholars have denounced the notion of evolution throughout the last hundred years or so. Darwin, evolutionary theory's founder, has been unfavorably looked on in spite of what he proposed as a rational theory backed by a substantial amount of observational evidence—one that has been repeatedly confirmed by many scientists since it was first proposed in the mid-nineteenth century. In this section, I intend to demonstrate that evolution is not only an established and highly regarded scientific theory but a truth confirmed by the Quran as well. I intend to support this claim while leaving no doubt as to the Quran's position on this topic. But before I do, we need to briefly understand the general process of evolution that governs the progression of life on Earth.

Evolution is a theory that, in principle, describes how life changes or morphs into newer forms in response to a dynamic external environment in a manner that enables life-forms to become better suited to survive and thrive in that environment. Evolutionary theory maintains that life has a common origin and that, for example, fish evolved into amphibians, which in turn evolved into reptiles, which in turn evolved into mammals, and which in turn finally evolved into humans. Evolutionary theory has been under examination, test, and verification ever since Darwin first proposed it in 1859 in his book *On the Origin of Species*. It's considered by virtually all scientists studying life on Earth to be a highly successful theory, a theory that's been widely substantiated and confirmed through countless fossil records, extensive anatomical studies, and advanced DNA analysis of many of life's past and present species. Anyone who accepts the truth of science today must also accept the fact that life evolved on our planet and that this evolution has led to the existence of our modern human species. With this overview, let's now examine the following verses:

> And there is in not a single mover on [or in] Earth [or the land], nor a bird that flies with wings, except that they are groups [or nations] like you [humanity]. We did not waste any part of the book.
>
> (6:38)

> And we [the god] surely created man from a lineage [or line] from wet clay [or soil, mud].
>
> (23:12)

> The one [the god] who made beautiful everything he created and started [or began] man's creation from wet clay [or soil, mud].
>
> (32:7)

> And [I, the god, swear] by a life and how he [the god] made erect [or straight].
>
> (91:7)

> And surely [the god] created you [humanity] in stages [or phases].
>
> (71:14)

> He [the god] is the one who created you [humanity] from wet clay [or soil, mud] and then later determined a time, a time clear [or known] to him, and then later you [humanity] doubt [the existence of the god].
>
> (6:2)

> And the god created every mover from water, so that some move on their stomachs, and some move on two legs, and some move on four legs. He [the god] creates what he wills. The god is surely completely capable of anything.
>
> (24:45)

The first of these verses is quite a revealing one. This verse has defied the standard interpretation because it talks about how other life-forms are *like us* and then talks about not wasting any part of a *book*. What does the verse mean by *like us* (*emtha'likum*: "like you, similar to you") and what exactly is this *book* (*kitab*)? The standard interpretation simply does not provide answers to these questions. If, however, we were to interpret this verse in light of evolutionary theory, then the verse becomes perfectly clear. When the verse says *groups* or *nations* (*ummem*: "nations, people, political bodies"), it is actually referring to what we scientifically know today as *species*. As noted earlier, *species* refers to a group of individuals who only interbreed with one another and not with members of another group. Thus, the Quran's use of the words *groups* (or *nations*) and *like you* is fittingly appropriate here.

The *book* the verse refers to is most likely a reference to a species' genetic code. In a surprisingly similar manner to the Quran, many modern-day scientists refer to this code as the "book of life" or the "library of life." A book is ultimately representative of *knowledge*. The genetic code, too, represents knowledge that defines and specifies a particular life-form, similar to how a food recipe defines and specifies a particular meal. A book is also composed of chapters, sections, paragraphs, sentences, words, and ultimately letters. In a similar vein, the genetic code is also composed of "letters." The letters that make up the genetic code are A, C, G, and T, representing the four nucleotide bases of a DNA strand: adenine, cytosine, guanine, and thymine. When grouped together, these letters make up genes. Genes in turn work individually and in groups to define specific traits, attributes, or functions of a particular life-form. The combination of all of the life-form's genes is called the genome, and this genome is stored on one or more chromosomes.[144] The genome can thus be thought of as representing the overall book, while the chromosomes can be thought of as representing chapters in the book. It's perhaps true that there isn't a better metaphor for the genetic code more apt than that of a book, and again, the Quran's choice for a word is highly precise and appropriate.

When the verse says that the god *did not waste* (*fur'rut*: "waste, throw away, neglect") *any part of the book*, it's actually referring to the commonality of the DNA code for all species. This commonality is a fact that has been scientifically verified and is now accepted as truth by virtually every living life-sciences specialist. When I use the term commonality, however, I use it in a somewhat loose sense, as there's always very minor variation among members of the same species as well as between members of various

---

144. If typed out, the human genome and its 3 billion letters would fill the pages of two hundred telephone directories.

species. For example, humans living today are 99.9 percent genetically similar. Only 0.1 percent of the genetic variation is responsible for how I am different from my neighbor and you from another person living on the other side of Earth. Species, too, are genetically very similar to a surprisingly large extent. It's really astonishing how all life, past and present, has shared this commonality ever since the existence of life's last common ancestor (LUCA) almost 4 billion years ago.

A rather amusing story in this regard was reported when the prophet Muhammad was once walking with a group of followers and passed by a collection of palm trees. The prophet stopped, gazed at the trees, and asked those with him to always love the palm tree, implying that palm trees were his followers' cousins.[145] When I used to come across this account, I would dismiss it as Muhammad being his usual kind self and asking his followers to love something that is not even human. But could the prophet have been alluding to something more insightful? If we accept that all life is related, then humans and palm trees share part of the overall genetic pool, which means that humans and palm trees are, in a sense, "cousins." Indeed, all of life is but a huge single extended family, a fact we now accept as scientific truth and alluded to by the prophet more than fourteen hundred years ago.

The last point I'll make about the first verse is its linguistic structure and how it can clearly be seen calling out all life-forms on Earth by using the phrase *there is in not a single* (*ma min*: "not one, not a single"). The verse then follows by establishing an association between that entire spectrum of life and the common book of life through the phrase *we did not waste any part of the book* ("not wasting" is synonymous with reuse, which in turn implies utilization of a common or shared resource).

The second verse talks about a *lineage* (*sulala*: "progeny, offspring, lineage") that ultimately led to the existence of man. This, too, is in agreement with our understanding of how past species evolved, leading to the modern human species. As noted earlier, the third verse used the word *started*, which, as I noted earlier, obviously implies a process and not an instantaneous happening. The fourth verse talks about how a life becomes *straight* or *erect* (*sow'wa*: "arrange, organize, put in order, set right, make straight"), a reference that most likely pertains to how modern humans have emerged from other hominids that existed throughout the past several million years who were not able to walk on two legs in an erect manner as we currently do. The fifth verse clearly states that man was created in *stages* or *phases* (*atwara*: "phases, stages, periods"), in agreement with evolutionary theory. When past Islamic scholars—who lived from when the Quran was first revealed to about 100 years ago, a period when most of the standard

---

145. The specific saying was "Cherish your father's sister (aunt), the palm tree."

interpretation was created—saw this verse, they must have assumed that the god created man in an "oven-like" manner and that man underwent different cooking stages, just as a loaf of bread would when baked. These scholars simply did not have the scientific knowledge we have today and thus could not have possibly conceived of the true meaning of this verse or that of the other creation verses. The sixth verse talks about a time lapse between our creation from wet clay and our current appearance.[146] This, too, is in agreement with our current scientific understanding that this time span was between 3.5 and 4 billion years (assuming the wet clay state in the Quran applies to LUCA and not to the muddy amphibian environment). The last verse was brought up earlier and clearly points to our watery origin. The word *mover* generally refers to insects and animals that live on land and has been used within the Quran to exclude fish and birds. This, again, is in agreement with our current scientific understanding that life moved from the sea to land some 400 to 600 million years ago, when atmospheric ozone (the molecule that protects Earth from life-damaging ultraviolet solar radiation) was available in sufficient quantities such that life could adapt to and further evolve on land.

I will conclude this discussion on evolution by citing another set of telling verses, which we touched on earlier in the section. In fact, if there were a single set of verses in the Quran that can be called "the evolution verses," these verses would certainly be it. Here's the expanded version of verse 32:7:

> *The one [the god] who made beautiful everything he created, and started [or began] the creation of man from wet clay [or soil, mud]. Then later made **his** progeny [or descendants] from a line from lowly [or menial] water. Then later made him straight [or laid him in order] and blew [or inspired] in him from his [the god's] essence [or soul, spirit] and made for you [humanity] the [senses of] hearing and seeing and wisdom [or intuition]; little do you [humanity] appreciate.*
>
> (32:7–9)

What we need to carefully study in these verses is the bolded pronoun *his* and try to uncover what this pronoun is specifically referring to. From the surface, it may seem that this pronoun is referring to *man*, but this

---

146. The word *from* in verse 6:2, as well as in other verses, should be understood to apply to the environment, such as saying that someone is from the South and not as in a cake is made from flour. This realization was what constituted my moment of enlightenment that I experienced while reading through the *Scientific American* article on evolution I mentioned in the Background and Introduction.

is not the case at all. It simply cannot be referring to man because we do not have descendants that can be considered to be a line or lineage that comes from lowly water. Nothing in our common experience supports such a conclusion.

We must therefore accept that what this pronoun is referring to is *the creation from wet clay* or, in other words, the life that was established from wet clay that in turn yielded a progeny (later in time) that came from lowly water, possibly referring to amphibians evolving from fish and occupying swampy or muddy areas. And so if we accept this logic, then we have a life—the origin of man as stated by the verses—that came from wet clay or soil, and it was this life that had *descendants* (*nasl*: "offspring, progeny, descendants, children") that in turn (and later in time) formed a *lineage* (*sulala*) that was associated with *lowly water* (*ma'in maheen*: "water that is menial or low"). This lineage thus progressed to become *straight* (*sow'wa*) and was inspired from within the core of the god (which, as I'll discuss in the next section, is a reference to man achieving a highly evolved state). Equating this inspiration by the god with being in a highly evolved state is supported by the fact that the verses associated the senses of hearing, seeing, and wisdom (or intuition) with this advanced state, since wisdom or intuition is understood to require a highly evolved mental and cognitive capacity (as well as an ample degree of emotional maturity). All this is further supported by the closing of the verses, which state that man is ultimately unappreciative of all this. Clearly, the verses are associating humans' lack of appreciation to the god with the backdrop of the substantial change and development needed for them to come forth from quite humble beginnings.

What is unquestionably evident from this set of verses is that *man* (who is called specifically out in these verses) was not created instantaneously but instead was associated with a creation that involved time progression (since the verses used *then later* twice), a process that involved a beginning (since the verses used *started*), a lineage (since the verses used *lineage*), and the existence of *progeny* (or descendants), also called out by the verses.

Supplemental Discussion I—More on the Gray Verses

One of the reasons why the vast majority of Muslim scholars have discounted evolutionary theory is probably due at least in part to a number of "gray verses," which deal with domains generally considered beyond our ability to fully comprehend and outside our immediate human reality.[147]

---

147. One of the comments I received during the book's review claimed that the Quran cannot be reconciled with science because the Quran presumes the existence of beings such as angels and "the evil one," of which there is no scientific evidence. If you find any discussion concerning such things stretching your comfort

One such account tells how the god instructed the angels to "prostrate to Adam" when two specific things come together. The first is when the god "lays man in order" (or when man becomes fully erect), and the second is when the god "blows" (or breathes, inspires) into man from within the essence (or core, spirit, soul) of the god. Other verses describe how Adam was "expelled from paradise" after being tempted by Iblees (the evil one, or Satan). And yet another set of verses describe how this evil one was also expelled from paradise and how he promised the god to forever deceive Adam and Adam's children to prevent humanity from ever returning to this special place.

I discuss these particular verses because I believe that the standard interpretation that relates to the creation of Adam cannot be completely discarded without such discussion. However, I do not delve into the religious or philosophical aspects or potential meanings of these verses because such discussion is outside the immediate scope and purpose of this book. As stated in the Background and Introduction, I intentionally minimized any discussion not directly related to the book's central theme, but also, I do so because these verses may ultimately belong within a domain of knowledge that lies beyond our full grasp and comprehension, outside of our known physical reality.[148]

So let's first discuss the verses that deal with the angels prostrating to Adam. Curiously, one of these verses (2:30) also refers to Adam as a "later one" (*khalifa*: "successor") or something that follows something else. The Arabic word for "later one," *khalifa*, comes from the root word *khelf*, which means "behind" or "after." By using the word *khalifa*, the Quran is clearly implying that Adam came *after* something else.[149] The verses fur-

---

zone, it may make sense to skip this section and return when you have finished reading through the entire book. Hopefully by that time you will have found the notion of the existence of a supreme being somewhat more plausible (if you already don't), and this section thus a bit more fathomable. As I stated earlier, the Quran is a book that's concerned with the totality of the human experience, and some of this experience, according to the Quran, falls into a richer domain of knowledge (or into a deeper level of meaning) beyond what can be explained through pure science alone. In my view, if science has taught us anything, it's that the more we know, the more we discover we do not (or cannot) know (see *The End of Discovery: Are We Approaching the Boundaries of the Knowable?* by Russell Stannard).

148. Recall the Quran's assertion in chapter 4 that our knowledge is but very little, as well as my proposition in the same chapter that our comprehension of true reality is, in all likelihood, either nonexistent or severely impaired.

149. This is further supported by verse 7:11, which reads *We [the god] have surely created you [humanity], then later we gave you your appearance, then later we asked the angels to bow to Adam.* The verse's use of *then later* following our species creation (in my view, this creation represents first life, or LUCA) and our appearance prior to asking the angels to bow to Adam (which I believe to be an act of

ther detail that this bowing or prostrating should not take place until after the occurrence of two specific events. As noted earlier, the first is when man is *laid in order* (or *erect*), and the second is when the god breathes into man from within the god's essence. As I pointed out, translating the Arabic word *sow'wa* as *lay in order* is not correct because it implies the false assumption that Adam was put together the same way that a toy is assembled. The translation of *sow'wa* as *straight* or *erect* is the correct one, in my judgment, and is the one that agrees with established science. This is supported by our knowledge that modern humans evolved from earlier humanlike species over millions of years, and these early hominid species did not walk completely straight on only two limbs as we do today.

What about the god breathing into Adam? What can this possibly mean? As I stated previously, the god cannot be thought of as "breathing" in a manner similar to how a human breathes. When the Quran uses such terms, a simple but perhaps natural reaction is to think of the god as a humanlike figure possessing humanlike attributes. This is a false and misleading conception that only hinders our ability to gain more knowledge of the god's "true" nature.[150] We also need to remember that the Quran was revealed to a rather simple and primitive people, long before humanity achieved practically any scientific advances. And so when these words are used by the Quran, they are meant only to communicate an idea, similar to how a metaphor normally serves such a purpose, and should never be thought of as representing the god's inherent reality.

Another possible reason why we normally attempt to summarize and trivialize things is because of our innate desire to want to fully understand anything and everything around us. We sometimes fail to accept or recognize that the universe (or more appropriately the multiverse in which our universe is but a bubble among countless other bubbles) we live in is perhaps a profoundly mysterious place. We only recently began to accept, based on the physics of quantum mechanics, that there may be real limits to what we can ultimately know, not because we haven't yet advanced far enough, but because there are inherent limits to this knowledge.[151]

So what can the god "breathing into Adam" actually mean? I believe

---

thanking, not of submission) is yet another clear statement that Adam's creation was not instantaneous.

150. I don't believe that we will ever understand the god's true nature. The best we can hope for is to understand aspects or attributes of the god that are only meaningful within the language of our known reality. In the end, all godly attributes are inherently only communicative and are not reflective of the god's true state (if indeed such a thing can even be ascribed to the god).

151. Within the sphere of life, too, things such as chance and randomness have played fundamental roles in life's existence and advancement.

that a partial answer to this question is that this breathing signifies a stage of human evolution in which the human brain evolved enough to want to better understand the meaning of the human existence within the larger universe and to achieve a better understanding of the Creator. At this point along the path of evolution, people *wanted* to ask some thoughtful questions in an attempt to achieve higher levels of meaning and content. I should note that I'm purposefully avoiding the use of the term *consciousness* here, because some biologists and zoologists have argued that animals, too, may possess consciousness, so there wouldn't be anything special about our species in this regard.

In my mind, "breathing into Adam" is not too different from saying something like "my heart belongs to my wife"—meaning, of course, that I love her very much (contrary to what she might think). Being a "language people," the Arabs undoubtedly created a rich set of such linguistic phrases to portray a wide spectrum of human emotion and expression. As I have stated, when such expressions occur in the Quran, they should be understood as being purely communicative and should not be interpreted in a strictly literal sense.

It's also important to note that the Quran used this same exact breathing expression in another case—that being of the biblical Mary, mother of Jesus.[152] The Quran reports how the god chose this woman of high virtue, who strived to protect herself against any unlawful sexual relationships, to become—miraculously, through the god's "breathing"—a virgin mother to a baby boy. This breathing was in the form of the angel Gabriel touching Mary, thus causing her to become pregnant with Jesus. There are a number of important points regarding the breathing expression in Mary's case that should help us better understand what the Quran meant by breathing into Adam. First, the breathing into Mary was not breathing in the literal sense but rather a metaphor for a different kind of action (that of touching). Second, this breathing took place within *our physical reality* and not within some mysterious otherworldly existence. And third, this breathing resulted in something that extended beyond that which was breathed into (the birth of the prophet Jesus). Considering this result is important because one can argue, based on the logic of the third point, that what these verses refer to is not related to Adam at all but to something "of Adam" (as in descendants of Adam, if we carry the analogy to the fullest extent).

Additionally, the verses of the Quran that deal with the angels prostrating to Adam are clear in that they describe a discussion that took place in the past and that this bowing should take place *when* the two events mentioned earlier in the section occur, at some point *in the future*. Thus, the linguistic

---

152. 21:91 and 66:12

structure of these verses simply does not support an instantaneous creation of man.[153] In my mind, if we accept that Adam was a human being who lived relatively recently in life's 4 billion years of evolution, then there is no conflict within the Quran between these gray verses and the verses I discussed in the previous section. If, however, we continue to assume that Adam was the first creation as the standard interpretation calls for, then we have to acknowledge inconsistencies in this regard.

The next set of verses I want to discuss deal with the purported expulsion of Adam from paradise. A superficial read of these verses may point to Adam being instantaneously created, placed into paradise, and later expelled from it to live on Earth after being deceived by the evil one. But, as I mentioned earlier, a superficial reading of the Quran is sometimes quite foolish. In fact, it has never ceased to amaze me how the Quran almost seems at times to *want* to trip and confuse those who only choose to read it thoughtlessly and halfheartedly without any intention of carefully studying it.

The key aspect I need to clarify is whether this paradise was a particular earthly garden or whether this was the "ultimate" paradise described in other places in the Quran. Here, too, the Quran uses the same word for both, but the language used by the Quran to describe Adam's paradise implies a rather mundane environment. Several Muslim scholars have in fact argued that the paradise that Adam was expelled from was just an earthly garden and not the ultimate paradise of the Quran. One of these scholars was an Egyptian named Muhammad Metwelli El-Shaarawi, generally considered to be one of the most knowledgeable and influential Islamic scholars of the twentieth century. In his Arabic book, *Stories of the Prophets and Messengers*, El-Shaarawi argues that the word *paradise* (*jen'na*: "paradise, garden") was used frequently in the Quran to denote any garden. He then asserts that the ultimate paradise is a place, based on the Quran as well as the prophet's teachings, from which none are expelled. El-Shaarawi thus believes that the paradise that Adam was banished from

---

153. The Quran uses the letter *fa* that implies an immediate result when talking about the angels prostrating to man following the god's directive (when man is laid straight and blown into, as noted in verses 15:29 and 38:72), which is why a superficial look will lead the reader to conclude that man's creation was an instantaneous event. However, the Quran also uses the word *when* where it talks about this directive. This clearly means that the creation of man and the hence prostration of angels for Adam were not instantaneous events (otherwise, it makes no sense for the Quran to use *when*). While this may be perceived as an inconsistency within the Quran, it offers an opportunity to explore a deeper meaning (which I will not get into here).

was just a special earthly garden, located on a hilltop (because the Quran uses the word "descend" when asking Adam to leave).

The Quran goes on to describe how the god provided Adam and his mate, Eve, with special provisions in this garden—as the god has done with many later prophets in the form of one or more "miracles"—and asked that they not eat from a particular tree (again, I will not go into the potential religious or philosophical meanings of this here). Adam was then tempted by the evil one (Eve had nothing to do with this temptation according to the Quran[154]) and disobeyed the god after much insistence and encouragement from this evil one (whom the Quran describes in verse 18:50 as a member of the jinn and not as an angel). Because of his disobedience, Adam was asked to leave this garden, so he descended from this hilltop to live a "normal" life in other places on Earth. Adam then asked the god for forgiveness, and the god accepted and immediately forgave Adam. He was then chosen by the god to become the first prophet to humanity. And so when Adam felt deeply saddened for disobeying his creator, little did he know that such disobedience paved the way for many positive things to come for him and the rest of humanity. Such a thing is undoubtedly so characteristic of human life![155]

I, for one, have no doubt that all this was a lesson for an inquisitive and special man, Adam, who lived relatively recently in human history and who appeared to possess a special sense of wonder and intellect.[156] So, after nearly 4 billion years of evolution, highly intelligent beings who are capable of great learning, exploration, and creativity came to be—as intended by the god, according to the Quran. These advanced beings would also prove able to affect their natural environment in ways no other living species had

154. 20:120

155. An important question that relates to this topic is this: Did Adam coexist with other humans? And if so, why does the Quran at times refer to humanity as the "children of Adam?" If we accept evolutionary theory, then Adam must have coexisted with other humans, and this very conclusion is also supported by the Quran in verses 17:70 (which implies that other Adam-like sentient or mindful beings existed but may have become extinct) and 2:30 (which implies that Adam was preceded by other "vengeful" humanoids).

156. In addition to possessing wonder and intellect, I maintain that Adam may have been *spiritually* genetically superior (meaning that Adam was more inclined to seek the god). This genetic superiority explains two things: The first is why the god "sequestered" Adam in a special protective place (paradise), possibly to shield him from any famine, war, or disease that may have been taking a toll on humans. The second answers the question of why most (if not all) monotheistic prophets, according to common religious tradition, come from Adam's line of descent. This genetic superiority may ultimately turn out to be what the Quran meant by *lay in order* or *straight*.

before or since. They would go on to learn languages, build cities, create cultures and civilizations, form political parties and governments, engage in wars, conquer new territories, exploit Earth's natural resources, and even advance to land on the moon. A good degree of complexity from various social interests and perspectives, with countless interactions and interdependencies, is also arising on what constitutes "right" and "wrong." So along the way, according to the Quran, the god deems it necessary to provide this particular species with help and guidance by outlining general principles of conduct and virtue to ensure some measure of stability, progress, and happiness for all. Most importantly, this god is interested in ensuring the survival and happiness of the human species, as well as the preservation and coexistence of all life on Earth.[157]

Supplemental Discussion II—Thoughts on Evolution

In this section, I will endeavor to provide some thoughts on evolution in general and of man's evolution in particular. I believe that many of us have been programmed into thinking that we're far better than any other living species on Earth, and so the notion of us emerging from apes is not only silly but quite demeaning and offensive as well (humans are genetically close to both chimpanzees and some ape species, but *ape* is a shorter word to write and equally effective in serving my purpose, so I'm going to stick with it).

I'm also going to divide the discussion into three components, with each raising some useful points to ponder when considering accepting or denying the notion of evolution. As I stated in the beginning of the book, perhaps no one was as opposed to the idea of evolution as I was, but I nonetheless managed to quickly reverse my thinking once I understood and accepted what I considered to be the truth. As someone once said, "It's certainly not a shame to make a mistake, but it is a shame to stay in one."

The first angle I want to take on the topic at hand has to do with what makes me human and how I am different from an ape. Here, the important idea I want to communicate is that of *totality*. Put very simply, I am what I am because of my totality, and this totality is distinctly and fundamentally different from that of an ape. As stated earlier, the genetic code of life is common to all living species on Earth. The fact that I share a good percentage of this code with an ape is, in my opinion, somewhat meaningless. I also share a percentage of my being with the sun in the form of common chemical elements. But can someone say in such a case that Ahmad is x percent sun or that the sun is y percent Ahmad? Clearly these are absurd

---

157. The general topic of whether our majestic universe came to be for the benefit of mankind constitutes one of the most intriguing questions today.

statements, and the reason they're absurd is because the sun and I are each defined by our respective totalities, not by the individual constituents of our beings. In a similar vein, to say that a human being is more than 95 percent ape or that an ape is more than 95 percent human is equally absurd. Some may want to counter this viewpoint by reminding me that humans evolved from apes and not from the sun. This, too, is not a completely truthful statement. The fact of the matter is that both man and ape came from a sun (recall our discussion on the supernova explosion 5 billion years ago that created our solar system). And this sun in turn came from other suns, which eventually trace their origins back in time to the big bang event that created everything in our universe. So if we're going to define something by uncovering where that thing comes from, then the big bang deserves all such credit.

A related point to this particular angle has to do with understanding how things are "slightly different" from each other and how this can be quite misleading within some contexts. Let me illustrate through an example. Within the realms of physics and mathematics, for instance, when I state that two different problems can be solved by two respective solutions that are 90 percent similar, it's clearly understood what this means. It means that the methods, logic, or operations used to solve these two problems have many things in common, and if I know how to solve one mathematical or physical problem, I most likely can solve the second one by employing a strategy similar to the first. Within the realm of chemistry, if I state that two elements or molecules behave 90 percent similarly to each other chemically and if I know what the chemical properties of one element or molecule are, I can reasonably predict what the chemical properties of the other element or molecule will be. Again, I do so by exploiting the fairly large degree of similarity that exists between the two entities.

Within the realm of biology and species, however, the notion of similarity takes on a completely different meaning. When I say that 90 percent of the genetic code is shared between two life-forms, I can conclude absolutely nothing about what one life-form might be from knowing what the other life-form is. This is because even very tiny differences within the genetic code can result in enormous differences in function. Think about it: all humans are 99.9 percent genetically similar, yet we're all so different from each other. (Although not all of these differences are due to genetics, I'm sure many of us have probably wondered if someone we disliked was actually part of the same human race!) We are also more than 96 percent genetically similar to chimpanzees (more than 98 percent by some estimates), yet, in several important respects, we and chimps can perhaps be perceived as coming from two entirely different worlds within this vast universe. Thus, to somehow conclude that apes and humans are only slightly different from each other is, I think, a somewhat misleading and highly inaccurate statement.

The next angle I want to think about deals with our perceived special status over and above that of an ape. The notion that we are "better" than apes has been promoted and widely accepted by many today. Contrary to that attitude, an ape—or any other living organism for that matter—is a truly beautiful creature that's been 13.7 billion years in the making, effectively the same length of time as I have been in the making (the same minuscule difference as between $100,000 and $100,037 in the case of the chimpanzee). We must fully recognize and accept that apes and humans are "cousins" and that both of us are part of a much larger family—the family of life on Earth. These views are not simply points of personal or philosophical discourse; they're indisputable facts!

The last point I want to make on the topic of evolution and why we humans should not think of ourselves as superior constitutes a rather humble reflection on the overall human experience thus far. And here I'm forced to be quite blunt: we—ironically by far the most cognitively advanced species on this planet—must face the shameful reality that we messed things up pretty badly for planet Earth and her inhabitants!

I mentioned earlier how one scientist has estimated that in less than three hundred years, our species will wipe out almost two-thirds of all other Earth species. Our species has also proven to repeatedly engage in terrible wars, horrific acts of genocide, unspeakable atrocities, and mass exploitation and humiliation of other humans. You could also argue that we, as a species, are generally indifferent to the plight of many other suffering humans around the world. How many of our fellow global citizens do we lose each and every day because of simple causes that are often preventable with just a little assistance? How many go blind? How many develop lifelong diseases? How many go hungry? How many have lost their livelihood because of water pollution? How many go without clean water? How many go without even basic schooling?

The point I'm obviously trying to make is that not only have we proven to be sadly indifferent to our natural environment—the only known livable place in the universe—but we have proven to be generally oblivious to the basic life needs of a great many members of our own species as well. So to continue to advocate the position that we're far better than apes and therefore could not have possibly emerged from them is reflective of a certain measure of pride and ignorance that's far from factual reality—a reality that's best captured by the Quran while communicating to man his "proper place" and how he should gauge being better than other forms of life, as the following verses so eloquently convey:

*We [the god] have surely created man in the best of classes.
Then we shall return man to the lowest of classes. Except those
who become enlightened and practice virtue; they will see an
endless [or uninterrupted] reward.*

(95:4–6)

8 Human Biology

Following the exploration of many intriguing aspects of the cosmos, our home planet, and life, we stop next at an equally intriguing domain a little closer to home: discoveries within the realm of human biology. In this chapter, we delve into the realm of human embryonic development and human genetics as well as explore a humanlike ability in ants. We will discover that the Quran has also provided a number of accurate scientific insights within these areas that demonstrate surprising agreement with established modern science.

Early Fetal Development

The Quran contains a number of verses that describe, in good detail, how a human being grows inside the mother's womb. While the choice of words used by the Quran in these descriptions may appear to us now to be somewhat simplistic, they are, nonetheless, accurate representations of what takes place as the fetus grows within the womb. Let's examine these descriptions through the following verses:

> He [the god] is the one who created you [humanity] from clay particles [or dust, sediment], and then later from nutfa, and then later from alaqa, and then later he exits you as a baby, and then later you become mature [or strong], and then later you become old, but some may die before that. However, all reach a preordained time [of death]. Hoping [or wishing] you [humanity] think [or exercise your mind, intellect] about all this.
>
> (40:67)

> Humanity, if you have doubts about the resurrection, then consider this: We [the god] created you from clay particles [or dust, sediment], and then later from nutfa, and then later from alaqa, and then later from a mudtha that has taken shape and that has not taken shape to show you [or so that you can sense and comprehend], and we leave in the wombs what we deem to

*a certain time, and then later we exit you as a baby, and then
later you become your strongest [or most mature], and some of
you may die, and some of you may reach a very old [or senile]
age so that they do not know [or comprehend] anything. And
you [Muhammad] see the land dry and dead, but if we provide
water she cracks and grows, and gives life to beautiful things.
That is because [or to say that] the god is the Haqq, and that
he surely brings life to the dead, and that nothing is outside the
realm of possibility for him.*

(22:5)

*And we [the god] surely created man from a lineage from wet
clay [or soil, mud], and then later we made him a nutfa in a
stable [or secure] and resourceful place, and then we created
the nutfa into an alaqa, so we created the alaqa into the
mudtha, so we created the mudtha into bones, and we covered
the bones with flesh [or meat], and then later we established
[him or her] into a different being. So blessed is the god, the
most beautiful [or fine] of creators.*

(23:12–14)

Let's discuss these verses sequentially, starting with an overview. You
may recall that in chapter 7 I talked about how the reference to clay particles and wet clay is actually a reference to the origin of life on Earth. In
these sets of verses, the Quran takes us twice back in time. The first time
is to the origin of life itself almost 4 billion years ago, and the second is
when we, as individuals, were born. We are here today because we were
individually born some decades ago and also because life itself was "born"
almost 4 billion years ago.

There is another important point I need to make before we begin our
examination. Clearly, these verses are not intended to provide a detailed
modern-day medical description of the fetal development process. Instead,
they represent more of a cursory overview or snapshot of a few notable
stops along the way, all while striving to emphasize a much more important point to the reader: plainly communicating the Quranic concepts of
change and evolution.[158]

---

158. Unlike evolution in biological systems, evolution in this context means the
ability for humans to live within future worlds or existences that are much richer
than our Earthly existence (which is referred to by the Quran as *el-hayat el-
dunya*: "the lowly life"). Also, see the last two sayings of On Paradise (in chapter
2, Prophetic Sayings).

It seems that what these verses are really driving toward, as is clearly evident from the second verse as well as from other verses in the Quran, is man's recognition and acceptance of future change and evolution by demonstrating past change and evolution. In other words, the Quran wants the reader to understand that a future higher or richer existence is not only possible or probable but perhaps even certain, given that our existence today, both as a species and as individuals, only followed a reality or being that was either completely unknowable or—to further emphasize the Quran's case—perhaps even utterly nonexistent.[159] Let's now begin to explore these verses.

According to the verses, the first stage in our development is something called a *nutfa* ("sperm, semen"), which comes from the Arabic word for "a drop." As indicated by the third set of verses, *nutfa* in this context is an entity that must immediately follow fertilization since it's "made" (*ja'al*) and since it resides in a "stable and resourceful place" (some have proposed the *nutfa* in these verses to be the zygote). In addition to its generic meaning as "a drop," *nutfa* is also known to signify the male's sperm or semen. In this case, however, *nutfa* should probably be understood to mean a generic drop (as in a small amount), given the general context of verse 40:67.

The next stage of fetal development according to these verses, *alaqa*, is a rather interesting one. This word is Arabic for "leech," and it usually refers to something that's attached or to something that hangs due to an attachment (*alaqa*: "leech; to attach to, to hang down, fasten to"). It's scientifically known today that following fertilization, the embryo, which is nothing more than a collection of a few cells at this point, travels down the fallopian tube, producing more cells and growing rapidly in the process. Several days after fertilization, the tiny embryo reaches the uterus, where it implants itself into the uterine wall before beginning to grow rapidly. The third set of verses describes this point of implantation as a *stable [or secure] and resourceful place* (*qarar*: "stable site, location, residence, or place;" *makeen*: "firmly established, solid, strong, deep-rooted, substantial"), which it is. Based on modern scientific understanding, prior to implantation, the young embryo develops special rootlike outshoots that will help it absorb oxygen and nutrients from the mother's blood, similar to how a plant absorbs nourishment from wet soil through its own intricate root structure. In addition to facilitating the nourishment function, these outshoots serve to implant the embryo securely within the uterine wall

---

159. Did we exist prior to our births? Did any living thing exist prior to the birth of life 4 billion years ago? Did the universe exist prior to the big bang? In many verses, the Quran encourages its readers to ponder questions such as these prior to doubting the possibility of a higher life within a richer future existence.

lining. By the end of the first week following fertilization, the maternal tissue heals over and covers the embryo with something like a dome that provides it with an extra measure of protection and anchoring, which is vital to the embryo's welfare given the incredible degree of growth and development the new being will soon undergo. So we can see that the choice of words used by the Quran and the general description provided (of this "drop" coming into a stable, secure, and resourceful place while becoming an *alaqa*), although appearing somewhat simplistic, nonetheless does provide an essentially accurate depiction of what takes place during early embryonic development.

The next stage of fetal growth, outlined in the second verse and third set of verses, is something called *mudtha*, which is Arabic for "being chewed" or "chewed repeatedly." The majority of interpreters now believe that this word was chosen based upon what they saw in pictures of a four-week-old human embryo. The claim was made that this four- or four-and-a-half-week-old embryo looks like a piece of chewed meat (perhaps more so if you're looking for a piece of chewed meat!) with its backbone region, known as the somites, looking awfully similar to teeth marks.

When I began researching the meaning of this word and discovered this particular explanation, I didn't believe it. So I purchased an embryology textbook to see for myself, and sure enough, the pictures of a four-week-old human embryo do depict something that looks as if it is being chewed, with noticeable "teeth marks" along the backbone area (I also discovered that early embryos of frogs, mice, and fish look "chewed" as well). As interesting as this perspective seems to be, I've now come to believe that *mudtha* does not refer to the actual shape of the embryo but rather to the embryo during the developmental phase that's marked by the appearance of the cartilaginous elements (also known as the cartilaginous rods) that constitute the precursors of embryonic bones. This interpretation is further supported by the third set of verses, where it states that the *mudtha* eventually becomes bones (possibly marking the onset of the development of the fetal skeletal structure). Cartilage is flexible connective tissue that is not as hard as bone or as soft and flexible as muscle and is usually found within the joints of the body as well as in the discs located between spine vertebrae. It's not difficult to see how this form of matter could easily be expressed as "being chewed" or "chewed repeatedly." In the second verse, *mudtha* is further elaborated on by stating that parts of it have *taken shape* (*mukha'laqa*: "taken shape, taken form") while others have not and that this process is important for us to make sense of things or to understand.

According to modern scientific knowledge, the development of the embryo involves five main cellular processes that build on each other as the embryo continues to grow with the progression of time. These processes are cell division, pattern formation, change in form, cell differentiation, and growth. Thus, in the second verse, where it mentions *taking shape* and *not taking shape*, it may be referring to the second, third, and fourth of these cellular processes. During the fourth cellular process, differentiation, embryonic stem cells begin to differentiate into other cells with specific functionality, such as into brain cells, pancreatic cells, kidney cells, and so on (the human body contains about two hundred different types of cells). Applying this particular understanding to the verse, we can probably conclude that the cells that have *taken shape* are the specialized organ and tissue cells, while the ones that have *not taken shape* are the stem cells yet to differentiate. The reference in the verse to making sense or understanding also follows logically, since we require the specific brain and specialized organ cells to develop the working organs and systems needed to provide the functionality required for our senses and cognitive abilities.

The third set of verses discusses how meat (or more appropriately, how muscle) covers the bones, which also takes place during the development of the young embryo. Scientists today understand that the muscle cells (actually the precursors to the muscle cells) migrate from the region of the somites to the regions of the limbs. They are then guided by the limb cells to specific sites within these limbs and eventually develop into muscle cells. As muscle cells continue their development, they attach to the bones and literally grow with the bones in a highly coupled and coordinated manner. The *different being* (*khel'qen akher*: "another being, different creature") mentioned by the third set of verses most likely refers to the embryo's completed state, now a miniature human being.

Reflecting on the astounding amount of change the single fertilized cell goes through in becoming this *different being*, a physician named Lewis Thomas writes in his book *The Medusa and the Snail* about the "miracle" of how a single cell becomes a human being and concludes, "The mere existence of that cell should be one of the greatest astonishments of the Earth. People ought to be walking around all day, all through their waking hours, calling to each other in endless wonderment, talking of nothing except that cell."[160]

This thoughtful (and humbling) sentiment has also been captured and echoed by the Quran in the third set of verses, saying, *So blessed is the god, the most beautiful [or fine] of creators.*

The Uniqueness of Fingerprints

Each of us possesses a unique set of fingerprints; they're not even the same between identical twins. The uniqueness of fingerprints is something we

---

160. Thomas, *Medusa and the Snail*, 156.

all accept today, but it is nonetheless a relatively recent discovery. Fingerprint uniqueness is also why fingerprint identification has become widely accepted all over the world ever since it was first adopted by Scotland Yard in the late 1800s. Although the Quran does not state this uniqueness explicitly, it does clearly allude to the special status of fingerprints in the following verses:

> Does man think that we [the god] cannot [or will not] gather his bones [referring to the resurrection]? Yes! We are surely able to put right [or reconstruct] his fingertips.
>
> (75:3–4)

These verses imply that reconstructing (from the word *sow'wa*) fingertips (*benan*: "fingertips") is more difficult than gathering bones, itself a monumentally difficult task that is almost impossible to comprehend.

Determining Fetal Sex

It has been scientifically accepted for some time now that it is the male's contribution that decides the sex of the offspring. This is because sperm contains both an X chromosome and a Y chromosome, while the female egg only contains an X chromosome. Upon fertilization of the egg by the sperm, the father provides one chromosome and the mother the other chromosome. If the result of this borrowing is an XY combination, the child will be male, and if the combination is XX, then the child will be female. The Quran captures the assigning of responsibility for the offspring's sex to the father in the following verses:

> Does man think that he is left without a purpose? Was he not once a nutfa from a gushing fluid? And then was an alaqa [the god] created and made straight [or completed] so that from **him** was made the two mates [or pair], the male and the female. Is he [the god] who did this not able to bring life to the dead?
>
> (75:36–40)

According to the rules of Arabic grammar, we must use a female pronoun when referring to a female form and a male pronoun when referring to a male form. The important question we want to explore in these verses is this: To what is the bolded *him* specifically referring to? It cannot refer to either *nutfa* or *alaqa* because both of these words are of the female form. It also cannot refer to the god because the Arabic word for *was made* (following *him*) normally refers to something that directly comes from something else (*ja'al*: "to make, render, cause to be or become"). And because it's inappropriate to think of human males and females coming directly from the god, the reference to the god must also be discarded (in addition, "the god" is not explicitly called out in these verses). From a strictly linguistic perspective, *him* can only refer to either of two things: the word *fluid* (*mena*: "sperm"[161]) or the word *male* (*theker*) that immediately follows *him*. In both cases, these verses are saying that it is the male's contribution that determines whether offspring are male or female. This insight is further supported by even more verses:

> And that man does not have [or earn] except what he has
> endeavored [or worked] for. And that his endeavors will be
> seen [or examined]. And then [the god] will hold accountable
> in the fairest of measures. And to your [Muhammad's] life giver
> is the final journey [or end state]. And that he [the god] made
> laugh and made cry. And that he [the god] made dead and
> alive. And that he [the god] created the two mates [or pair], the
> male and the female, from a nutfa when discharged.
>
> (53:39–46)

We can see that these verses explicitly call out the two sexes (the previously noted *theker* and *untha*: "female") and that they associate the creation of these two sexes with a *nutfa*, which, as I mentioned earlier, is also generally translated as sperm. Translating *nutfa* as sperm is quite appropriate here, since the verses state that this *nutfa* is being *discharged* (*tumna*: "poured forth"[162]). In addition, the Quran does not explicitly call out the two sexes within the context of a creation beyond the verses presented in this section.

Talking Ants

Yes, ants apparently can talk. Scientists have realized for quite some time now that ants, as well as other insect species, communicate among themselves. This communication mostly takes place through excreting special chemical signals or through certain bodily movements (such as when bees "dance"). However, it's also been recently discovered that some insect species, such as ants, can also communicate using sound via a process known as *stridulation*, wherein the insect rubs together select body parts and creates a sound signal. This phenomenon has been recently presented in an article by Lewis Smith titled "Hills Are Alive with the Sound of Ants—Talking to Each Other" (*Sunday Times* [London], February 6, 2009), which discusses

---

161. Penrice, *Dictionary and Glossary*, 217; also see Baalbaki, *Al-Mawrid*, 1177.
162. Parekh, *Complete Easy Dictionary*, 223.

surprising discoveries related to how ants talk to each other through this sound mechanism.

The Quran mentions this intriguing fact—one impossible for anyone to discover until the invention a few decades ago of sensitive electronic listening devices—in a story where king (and prophet) Suleiman (the biblical King Solomon) was crossing an "ant valley" with his soldiers. Prophet Suleiman came very close to a particular ant and heard her calling her fellow ants, warning them against getting crushed by the approaching human army. Now, according to the Quran, as a prophet Suleiman was given several extraordinary abilities, including the ability to talk with birds, summon powerful creatures, and hear the talk of ants, as these verses illustrate:

> *And when they [Suleiman's army] came upon the valley of the ants, an ant **said**, "Ants! Enter your dwellings so that Suleiman and his army do not unknowingly crush you." So he [Suleiman] smiled with laughter from what she **said**, and [Suleiman] asked, "My life giver, help me thank you for your gift that you have given me and given my parents, and that I do right in the way that you accept."*
>
> (27:18–19)

First, I'll need to note here that all special abilities mentioned in these verses were only specific to Suleiman, while the ants went about being just ordinary ants. In these verses, the word *said* (from *qul*: "say, tell, speak") has been associated with our ant in two separate instances (both bolded), thus clearly implying a communication through sound. If this communication was in the form of a physical movement or a sort of chemical excretion, the verses would have used the word "did" in place of the second mention of *said* (the verses could also have used "he saw" instead of "she said"). It's also important to note that the verses seemed to want to specifically call out the phrase *from what she said* at the risk of being somewhat redundant, since the verses could have been made more concise by deleting this phrase while keeping the meaning the same. It's also worth noting that even though stridulation results from the insect rubbing different body parts together, the actual communication is carried through the means of sound and not in the actual movement of the insect itself.

It's really astonishing how a creature so tiny and delicate not only moves, builds, and fights for most of its life but also "talks." I would *love* to know what an ant's daily messages, aspirations, and complaints actually are.

But on second thought, perhaps I would not. We don't need anyone to turn in yet another mind-punishing reality TV show, do we?

9 Technological Achievements

Sometimes I find it truly wondrous how an event that took place 13.7 billion years ago (the big bang) has led to the creation of the most elementary forms of matter; which in turn has led to the development of countless stars and galaxies; which in turn has led to the creation of a variety of chemical elements; and which in turn has finally led to the development of numerous planets, moons, comets, and asteroids. At least one of these planets turned out to be very fortunate and became habitable. It allowed for the existence of an abundant amount of liquid water over very long periods of time, an absolute precondition for the creation and development of life. This life adapted and evolved and eventually led to the development of the most astonishing organ in the known universe—the human brain. This remarkable organ went on to conceive of and bring to life an incredible array of complex devices that were used to facilitate many discoveries and greatly broaden the brain's understanding of the innermost secrets of the universe from which it came—an understanding so extraordinary that it has thus far set our species apart from anything we've come across in this grand universe we inhabit.

In this rather short chapter, I talk about a few of mankind's most impressive technological achievements attained since our species first walked this Earth some two hundred thousand years ago while also presenting a number of verses from the Quran. It will become evident throughout the discussion that the Quran has foretold these achievements many hundreds of years prior and has done so with a considerable degree of clarity.

The Flying Machine and Airplane Travel

As I stated in the Background and Introduction, discovering the true meaning of the "airplane verse" had an important influence on me, helping to convince me to dedicate a number of years to researching the scientific aspects of the Quran. This verse was also important in the sense that it confirmed for me the need to sometimes ignore the apparent meaning of a particular verse and focus instead on the deeper one. In other words, it's because of the deeper meaning that the verse exists in the first place, with the apparent meaning being nothing but a mirage.

This perspective does not apply to every verse, of course, and in many cases we must take what's said at face value. So, for example, when verse 17:37 says *Do not walk the earth with pride, for you will neither penetrate the earth nor will you reach the mountains through your height,* we must interpret this as the apparent meaning implies—that humanity must always feel a sense of humility. In the case of the verse we'll discuss shortly, however, the apparent meaning makes little sense, while the deeper one is highly insightful and telling. I need to clarify here, though, that when I refer to the deeper meaning of a science-related verse, I am referring to the scientific insight provided by that verse and whose meaning is later confirmed through established science. On the other hand, the deeper meaning of the Quran—the spiritual depth I alluded to earlier—is different and clearly not the subject matter of this book.

An important consequence of this understanding is that we (or anyone interested in the Quran) should not feel as if we have to find a proper interpretation for every verse in the Quran. In my opinion, it's better to not have an interpretation available for an unclear verse than to have an incorrect one assigned to it. An unclear verse will show its meaning when its time has come, as the prophet frequently proclaimed when stating that "the Quran reveals itself in time." This cautionary note may sound somewhat obvious to some, but the emphasis is necessary given the many flawed interpretations of verses out there—and some of these verses are rather significant ones. Let's now return to the topic at hand and examine the "airplane verse," as I call it:

> Do you [Muhammad] see how the god has put to humanity's
> benefit what is on Earth [or the land], and the ships travel
> in the ocean through [or by] his will, and he holds the sema'a
> so that it does not fall to Earth [or the land], except for what
> he has permitted? Surely, the god is filled with mercy and
> compassion toward mankind.
>
> (22:65)

As we've done during prior discussions, let's begin by studying the verse's key words and phrases. Let's start by examining the phrase *and he holds the sema'a so that it does not fall to Earth* (*yumsik*: "hold, grasp, grip;" *sema'a*: "sky;" *teq'a*: "fall, drop;" and *ardh*: "Earth, land"). Let's also remember, based on a discussion in chapter 5, that *sema'a* can be used to signify anything above. Also, the verse talks about ships that travel the ocean just prior to this, and in general the verse is talking of things that are of service and benefit to mankind. The verse also associates mercy and compassion (*ra'ouf*: "merciful, kind;" *raheem*: "compassionate, gracious") when talking about the verse in general but especially with reference to *holding the sema'a*, since the reference to mercy and compassion immediately follows. The combination of all of these clues led me to believe that *sema'a* was, in fact, a reference to some sort of travel-related flying machine, such as an airplane. In chapter 5, we learned how stars manufacture chemical elements and also that these chemical elements are of vital importance to our existence and continued survival. During that discussion, I mentioned how the Quran's use of *colors* sealed the verses' meaning in my mind and elevated my confidence from 90 percent to 100 percent with regard to the verses' true meaning. The airplane verse presents a similar example.

The airplane verse is placed in a chapter titled "The Hajj," (*hajj* being the Arabic word for pilgrimage). Pilgrimage is the act of traveling to the city of Mecca for about a ten-day period, during which Muslims circle the Ka'ba (the holy structure mentioned in chapter 2) and chant their love and devotion for the god, a sight most of us have probably seen on TV or elsewhere. Today, approximately 2 million Muslims perform the religious duty of hajj every year, and they travel mostly by airplane. It's also because of this trip that the word *mecca* has become commonly used in the English language to denote any important destination or special gathering place.

You may perhaps be wondering what significance placing a verse in a particular chapter has and why some interpreters (including myself) attempt to read something into that. To understand why this is so, we should recognize that, in general, the title of a particular chapter in the Quran is strongly related to the chapter's special theme or key point. This understanding has been recognized and accepted by many past and present Quranic scholars and interpreters. Since the title of the chapter that contains the airplane verse is "The Hajj," the special theme must be understood to be that of pilgrimage and of travel and, as I stated earlier, the vast majority of those who have ever performed hajj have done so via traveling. So when we endeavor to better understand what is meant by *sema'a* in the verse, we must keep the backdrop of travel in mind.

Some readers may think that perhaps what the Quran is referring to here is something like a meteor, and it's these types of objects that the god holds from falling to Earth, except for what he has permitted. Even though this suggestion can be entertained on the surface, the context of the verse is clearly that of things that benefit mankind and of travel. Meteors are obviously not related to travel, and it's difficult to imagine how falling meteors can benefit mankind, especially since a meteor the size of a single mountain can literally destroy our entire species, along with perhaps most complex surface life on our planet, as happened some 65 million years ago when an asteroid the size of Mount Everest slammed into Earth, wiping out the dinosaurs along with 65 percent of all living species in the process.

Thus, interpreting *sema'a* as a meteor does not yield a good or plausible explanation.

The Invention of Great Ships

Just as the Quran has predicted man's utility of future flying machines, the invention of great seafaring ships has also been foretold. The Quran contains numerous references to boats and ships (about twenty in all), but all these references, with the exception of the verses we'll discuss in this section, take on the form of a single word that usually translates into "boat" or "ship." In two instances, however, the Quran uses a markedly different type of description for the ship. In the first, the verses read as follows:

> And of his [the god's] signs are the ships in the sea that look [or
> appear] like mountains. If he wills, the wind will be calm [or
> absent] so that they remain motionless on the surface.
>
> (42:32–33)

Now, this description, which occurs only once in the Quran, is a completely new description for ship. The verses describe these particular ships as looking or appearing *like mountains* (*a'alam*: "higher mountains, banners"[163]).[164] The verses also associate *wind* (*reeh*) with the ships, so they must obviously be some sort of sailing vessels.

We all know that ship construction methods and techniques have advanced considerably since the Quran was revealed. Along with this advancement came an increase in ship size in all dimensions, including height, which became greater because of a taller mast. This advancement started around the fifteenth century and continued over the next several hundred years. During the fifteenth century, ships were built with a second mast; a third mast was added later. Because more masts allow for a greater number of sails, and since these sails are the primary means by which large ships gain the power needed to move in the water, the additional masts allow for larger and faster ships. By the middle of the fifteenth century, three masts became standard on the larger ships of the day, and by that century's end, the ship's main mast was also discovered to be able to hold a second smaller sail, which, when added, provided further wind power and speed. Also, up until the sixteenth century, ship masts were made from a single tree trunk. However, from the sixteenth century onward, ships required masts that had to be taller and thicker than what can be accommodated

---

163. Parekh, *Complete Easy Dictionary*, 216.
164. *A'alam* best translates to "rising above all else," but it's been used to denote mountains due to their great heights.

through a single tree trunk. To achieve this additional height, masts were built from up to four "sections," which were also referred to as masts. The combination of taller masts and multiple larger sails constituted huge benefits for ships and helped support the construction of larger, mightier ships and faster long-distance sea voyages. This development also occurred during the Renaissance, when a number of European powers emerged and constructed their fleets of powerful ships in search of new trade and raw materials, as well as to gain regional and global domination.

This leap in shipbuilding technique around the fifteenth century is further evidenced by the fact that prior to the end of the century, the typical merchant ship possessed a gross tonnage of no more than 250 tons.[165] However, shortly thereafter, ships were constructed with gross tonnage specifications that approached 1600 tons, representing an almost sevenfold increase. For example, *Great Harry* of 1514 was a four-mast ship that possessed a 1500-ton gross tonnage and was able to carry seven hundred men, specifications the likes of which the world had not seen before. Of course, many types of ships existed prior to and during the time of the revelation of the Quran, but they all lacked the tall masts and grand appearance that characterized the later ships of the fifteenth and sixteenth centuries (and beyond). It can thus be reasonably said that the sailing ships of these centuries were (or can be thought of as representing) great sailing ships that *look [or appear] like mountains.*

The next kind of ship description provided by the Quran is also mentioned only once and appears to represent an even grander type of ship, as the following verse—which we first met in chapter 1—illustrates:

> *And to him [the god] belong the established ships in the sea that look [or appear] like mountains.*
>
> (55:24)

Let's carefully study this short and rather curious verse. First, the verse employs the word *established* (*insha'a*: "establish, create, produce, manufacture, build up") to describe this new ship. As stated in previous chapters, *establish* takes on a very specific meaning within the Quran. *Establishment* has also been used within modern Arabic in recent times to denote things that require a substantial level of effort, such as what's involved in manufacturing or processing. Also, the Quran does not mention *wind* in, or anywhere near, this verse. The phrase *to him belong* (from the Arabic word *lehu* and used to signify possession: "to him, for him") has also been

---

165. The gross tonnage is a measure of the ship's cargo-carrying capacity.

added, but what has not changed from the previous verse is that these ships also *look [or appear] like mountains.*

Let's talk about the phrase *to him belong* first. Within the Quran in general, it's been clearly communicated through many verses that *everything* belongs to the god. However, when the Quran explicitly states that something belongs to the god, it usually refers to the grandest of possessions. These include things such as the notions of life and death, the entirety of creation, and so on. To associate a belonging to the god with that of a mere ship or type of ship is something quite strange and unexpected, based on how other belongings have been referenced within the Quran. Thus, this ship is clearly special.[166]

Next, let's consider the word *established*, which we've met in several verses thus far.[167] The Quran almost always uses *established* or one of its derivates (another word that's structurally slightly different but that implies essentially the same meaning) to denote a difficult or laborious process. For example, such derivatives have been used to describe the resurrection, the process of creating life from death. In other verses, *established* was used to describe the beginning and subsequent development of life itself. Again, to associate *established*, given its typical use within the Quran, with a mere ship is rather surprising and somewhat difficult to understand. Added to all this, the Quran chose a rather curious word for *ship* (*jareeya* from *jer'ee*: "flowing, streaming, running"). *Jareeya* usually implies rapid or extended movement that, when coupled with the lack of wind, further supports the belief that the ships cited by verse 55:24 are modern engine-driven ships. There is another important point to mention here with regard to the verse's location within the Quran. This verse is located in the Quran's chapter of "The Rahman," which I first addressed in chapter 1. As I noted then, Rahman is one of the names or core attributes of the god and usually translates into "the one with mercy, compassion, or kindness." We also learned that within the chapter of the Rahman, the god enumerates blessings and gifts bestowed upon humanity and continually asks, *So which of your life giver's gifts do you deny?* with *you* being a reference to humanity in general.

In my mind, the confluence of all these clues points to the intriguing possibility that the ships we're discussing here are akin to something like

166. Of the sixty or so instances of the explicitly called-out "belonging" in the Quran, forty-three pertain to the "heavens and Earth," five to "all strength," four to "the god's virtuous names," two to "life and the afterlife," two to "the east and the west," one to the "highest example," one to "all intercession," one to "everything," and one to "all of Earth and what's within."

167. See verse 6:98 in The First Living Ancestor (chapter 7), verses 53:32 and 11:61 in The Origin of Humanity (chapter 7), and verses 23:12–14 in Early Fetal Development (chapter 8).

modern cruise ships. A cruise ship is generally recognized as a floating city on the surface of the ocean. It can usually accommodate a few thousand passengers at a time, generate an ample amount of electricity (enough to power a small town in the United States), produce its own fresh water from sea water, and recycle its own waste, among many other modern engineering marvels. In fact, I recently learned that a newly launched class of cruise ship was so large (and surely equally so complex) that it weighed the equivalent of 430 jumbo jetliners! All these factors undoubtedly make these ships one of the most successful and impressive technological achievements undertaken by humans to date.

Given the general context of the Quran's chapter of the Rahman, along with the understanding that the ships we're discussing in this section are, in fact, representative of something like cruise ships, we can perhaps reasonably conclude that these ships are, in the eyes of the Quran, one of the god's (or, more appropriately, of the Rahman's) most generous gifts to humanity.

And indeed they are.

10 Precision and Geometry

Our universe is an amazing place, which is in large measure due to how the two concepts of precision and geometry have shaped it. Precision and geometry are not considered stand-alone sciences per se but rather constitute important components of many natural sciences. In this chapter we explore these two fascinating areas, which have played a significant role in defining the universe we live in, along with our sense of reality within it. Throughout our discussion, we'll discover that the Quran has alluded to this importance and has done so many years prior to modern science's full comprehension of and appreciation for precision and geometry's pervasiveness and mystery.

Precision

Most of us may think of precision as something like "Meet me at the golf course at 7 a.m. tomorrow" or "How many packets of sugar would you like in your coffee?" Although these are valid examples of precision, there's more to understand about this vital concept. So what does precision really mean? And why is it so important?

Back when I started my career as an electrical engineer more than twenty years ago, I once had the opportunity to work at a particular government facility to install and commission a special satellite communications system I helped design. After working at this facility for several weeks, I was invited by my hosts to take a short tour of the building, during which I was introduced to a special room. This particular room, which was filled floor to ceiling with all sort of electronics, turned out to be home to a large number of highly accurate time clocks known as cesium clocks, which play a vital role in keeping time.

Cesium is one of the natural chemical elements found in our universe (chemical symbol Cs) and was discovered in 1860 by two German chemists through spectroscopy, the science we learned about in chapter 5. Because of its relatively low melting point, cesium possesses an interesting property: although it is classified as a metal, it is normally only found in the liquid state at near-room temperatures (similar to mercury, the element used in thermometers). However, the cesium atom possesses an even more intriguing property that allows it to function as a very accurate time keeper. It's hard for us to fully appreciate this, as humans are accustomed to time accuracies in the seconds or, in special competitive athletic situations, a few fractions of a second. Imagine, however, if we can divide a time interval of one second into 9 *billion* smaller pieces. Now further imagine that we can produce these same 9 billion tiny intervals each and every time (second) without any one second turning into 9 billion plus one, or 9 billion minus one, of these tiny intervals! This is exactly what these cesium clocks do naturally. These clocks produce an astonishingly precise and consistent number of intervals each and every time, which is the reason why they're used as our planet's time reference. If you have ever used a global positioning system (GPS) receiver or device, such as that used for automobile navigation, then you've come in direct contact with these clocks.

Another striking example of precision can be found in molecules. Molecules are independent entities that contain a group of atoms bound together, within the molecule, through one or more types of bond. Because of this, molecules can be expressed by a particular chemical formula that illustrates the types and quantities of the different atoms that make up a particular molecule. So the water molecule, for instance, is a molecule that contains two hydrogen atoms (represented by the symbol H) and one oxygen atom (represented by the symbol O), hence the molecular formula H_2O for water.

One particular class of molecules is organic molecules (molecules that contain the element carbon). Organic molecules possess individual properties that enable them to carry out special functions. It turns out that if we wanted to make a particular kind of organic molecule, one with a specific function, we need to define two parameters in a precise manner. The first parameter is the precise number of atoms for each type of element contained in the molecule, and the second is the precise three-dimensional spatial arrangement for the different atoms that make up the molecule. If you keep the types and number of atoms that make up a molecule the same, for instance, and only change the three-dimensional atomic spatial arrangement, you potentially end up creating a different organic molecule with an entirely different molecular identity and associated function.

Comparing atomic "ingredients" to molecular products shows us another curious aspect of molecules. When individual atoms come together to form a molecule, the molecule assumes new properties that are sometimes distinctly different from the individual properties of the atoms that make up the molecule. A good example of this change in functionality can be found in the water molecule, H_2O. We all know what water is, and we also know that one of its main properties is its ability to put out fires. Interestingly, though, the elements that make up water are either highly explosive (the hydrogen component) or play a vital role in the burning process of combustion (the oxygen component). In an intriguing way, a new property "emerges" with the water molecule that was absent prior to water's individual molecular constituents coming together. Emergence is quite important and has played a vital role in shaping and defining many important natural properties and system behaviors within our universe.[168]

The idea of emergence also makes the notion of totality easier to understand and embrace. If you recall the discussion on totality from chapter 7 —how some things must be defined by their wholeness and not by their individual components—you can probably see how totality applies so fittingly to the example of the water molecule. One could certainly never have guessed that water could be used to carry out a function that's not only different from the behavior of its individual constituents but entirely opposite to those behaviors! The totality of water is thus what defines what water is, not the characteristics or behavior of its individual components.

And while we're on the general topic of molecules, let's take a moment to admire their relevance to life. It's quite fascinating how, from among millions of organic molecules that exist, only a few hundred or so have been used for making life on our planet. This means that life clearly preferred to become established and evolve through only those molecules, the so-called "molecules of life" initially mentioned in chapter 7. Equally fascinating is another selective force of life known as life's chirality, or "handedness preference," which has also become a strong influencing factor in how life evolved on Earth.[169]

In summary, precision is context sensitive and can mean different things in different circumstances. Sometimes precision can mean "two and a half teaspoons of sugar," and sometimes it can mean "exactly 9 billion oscillations per second," while at other times it can mean "100 atoms of carbon, 12 atoms of nitrogen, and 14 atoms of oxygen" arranged in *this* three-dimensional spatial configuration. When it comes to our larger universe, however—and how it evolved from the moment of the big bang until the present time, and how during this process life itself was conceived—the concept of precision takes on a more profound and mysterious construct.

---

168. In addition to the important properties of pressure and temperature emerging from the collective action of smaller constituents, some scientists now believe that even more fundamental universal properties, including those of space and time, may very well turn out to be emergent as well.

169. Chirality describes objects that cannot be superimposed on their mirror image. Our left and right hands are famous examples of chirality (it's not possible to wear a left glove on a right hand, for instance). Within the realm of the molecules of life, chirality means that certain molecules are "left-handed," while others are "right-handed." The origin of life's choice for chirality is still unknown and a topic of debate among scientists.

It turns out, as scientists continue to discover, that precision is a fundamental aspect or defining attribute of our universe and of our very existence. A striking example of this is in the discussion of the big bang event in chapter 5, where I mentioned that scientists believed that the ratio of antimatter to matter at a particular moment shortly after the big bang was 1 billion to 1 billion and one. This is the same ratio as $10 million to $10 million and a penny. It is astounding that it appears to be quite unimportant (would we care if we were short a penny after being handed $10 million?), yet we owe our existence—as well as the existence of everything material we can see, hear, or feel in the larger universe—to this tiny difference.

Cosmologists and physicists continue to ask why the fundamental building blocks of the universe possess the properties they do in the precise quantities they do and what effect such precision has had on the existence and evolution of everything. Consider, for example, the electron, one of nature's most fundamental particles. Every electronic gadget operates because of the role the electron plays in creating electricity. Electricity, in turn, exists because the electron has a certain property called *charge*, and this charge is a precise quantity that's exactly the same for each and every electron in nature. Would the universe we inhabit today be the same if this precise quantity for the electron turned out to be different from what it is?

An interesting book that discusses the notion of precision in the grander universe is *Just Six Numbers*, authored by Martin Rees, a well-known British cosmologist. In it, Rees argues how the precise quantity of six particular cosmological attributes has shaped how our universe came to be. Here, too, Rees wonders if the universe would be the same if any of these six numbers were to be even slightly different. There are many such examples of how precision has become so important, including how precision has impacted the existence of our very beings. In fact, the notion of why our universe appears to be so fine-tuned has been the basis of much debate among scientists and philosophers over the years. On the one hand, proponents of this perspective (that the universe is fine-tuned) argue that such delicate precision is intentional so that intelligent beings such as ourselves can emerge.[170] The other perspective, equally interesting, argues that our universe is but one of an infinite number of universes out there, and so there's bound to be at least one universe where the physical properties take on the precise quantities they do to allow for an existence such as ours. According to this perspective, there's nothing special about our existence,

---

170. Scientists and philosophers denote the sum of all coincidences that have led to the life-enabling universe we inhabit as the *anthropic principle*.

as we were fortunate enough to have stumbled upon a universe where everything was "just right."

Interestingly, the Quran seems to take the middle road between these two perspectives. On the one hand, as we'll see shortly through several verses, our universe was designed to be fine-tuned. However, the Quran also seems to imply in several other verses that our universe may be just one out of a much larger set of universes, worlds, or levels of existence (recall our discussion of bubbles and the multiverse from chapter 5). Precision's importance in the Quran can be seen through the following verses:

> *And [the god] created every single thing through impeccable*
> *precision [or through an overwhelming degree of fineness].*
>
> (25:2)

> *And we [the god] estimated [or calculated], and how precise [or*
> *fine, accurate] our calculation [or estimation] was!*
>
> (77:23)

> *The god knows what every female carries, and what is lessened*
> *in the womb and what is increased, and everything in the eyes*
> *of the god is a precise quantity [or exact measure].*
>
> (13:8)

> *Indeed, everything we [the god] created, we created precisely*
> *[or exactly measured].*
>
> (54:49)

It's evident from these verses that the Quran's emphasis on precision (*tuqdeer*: "estimation, assessment, appraisal, or evaluation of an amount, quantity, or number") is in agreement with our current understanding of precision's importance. The first verse emphasizes the importance of precision by using both of the words *qada'rahu* ("estimated, assessed, appraised") and *tuqdeer*. Additionally, when the words *qada'rahu* and *tuqdeer* immediately follow each other, as they do in verse 25:2, they communicate the maximum exaggeration of meaning for "estimation," which is why I translated them in the manner in which I did. The first verse also uses the term *every single thing* (*kul'lu sha'i*: "everything, all things") when making mention of *tuqdeer*. It's perhaps fair to assume that the importance of precision could not have been known, or at least not fully appreciated, by those living fourteen hundred years ago. They certainly could not have known how precise things really are, something we'll continue to discover well into the future.

Geometry

Most of us have probably been exposed to geometry during our middle or high school years. The geometry we'll be discussing here, however, relates to the shape of things, or how things appear in three-dimensional space. Just as precision is a fundamental aspect of our universe and of our existence, the concept of shape also appears to be equally important and fundamental.

Shapes range from the simple, such as the two-dimensional shape of a circle or square, to the more complex, such as the shape of a house or a mountain. Sometimes, however, shapes become so complex that they fall outside of our normal four-dimensional space-time reality. As mentioned in chapter 3, a new branch of physics called string theory attempts to uncover the most fundamental building blocks of the universe and proposes these building blocks to be nothing more than tiny vibrating strings. Interestingly, these vibrations are also believed to follow, or trace, a complex nine- or ten-dimensional shape that falls outside of our normal three-dimensional existence. In other words, according to this new, untested theory, our existence requires a specific shape for the vibrations of these strings—perhaps the most fundamental constituents of matter—in dimensions beyond that of our usual space and normal physical reality.[171]

Further supporting the importance of shape, Albert Einstein, in his general theory of relativity, explained the force of gravity through the shape of the four-dimensional space-time fabric. According to general relativity—a widely tested and accepted theory—things fall to Earth because of the particular curvature of the fabric of space-time, much like how little marbles fall toward a heavy bowling ball when the ball is placed in the middle of a stretched sheet of cloth.

We also learned in chapter 7 of the crucial role water plays in enabling carbon-based life in our universe. This, too, is facilitated through the water molecule's *V* shape. Without this special shape, with the oxygen atom at the apex and the two hydrogen atoms on either side, water would not have been able to play the important role it has played.

In fact, the role geometry plays in our universe may be so prevalent and so significant that some scientists believe that geometry is possibly why the elementary particles of the universe—along with how these particles drive the physical laws of nature—take on the specific physical properties that they do.[172]

The concept of shape applies not only to the domains of physics and mathematics but to the sphere of life itself. Organic life, the type of life on Earth, literally "works" through the facilitation of shape. For instance,

---

171. Yau and Nadis, *Shape of Inner Space.*
172. Lisi and Weatherall, "Theory of Everything."

the essential biochemical reactions so fundamental to life processes are all dependent on molecular shape. Important entities involved in these processes and interactions include proteins (one of the most important biochemical entities within a living organism), cell receptors, and neuro-transmitters, among many others. These entities simply cannot do their jobs if it weren't for their precisely chosen shapes. Slightly change the three-dimensional shape of a protein by slightly changing the genetic code that holds instructions for that protein, for instance, and the protein does not fold properly and thus ceases to function in the way it must to keep things running in a smooth and healthy manner for the overall organism.

A special type of protein, called an enzyme, provides a nice example that illustrates shape's importance to running things smoothly. Enzymes are quite important because they facilitate and expedite numerous reactions within a living organism and can speed up reactions by a factor of a million or more. Without enzymes, the food we eat would not be digested in hours but in weeks or perhaps even months instead. Enzymes, too, work through the facilitation of shape (an enzyme's highly specific shape-matching capability with a particular substrate is exactly why enzymes can speed up reactions so much), so they are possibly the perfect example of how important shape is to the essence of life. In addition to proteins and enzymes, the all-important phenomenon of *signaling* within biological organisms is also based on shape. Signaling is a vital process that lies at the core of life and can be thought of as a sort of information superhighway within a living organism. (Can you imagine what life would be like today without TV, cell phones, or the Internet?)

Finally, yet another stunning example of shape's influence within the realm of life has to do with what's known as the *adaptive immune system*. Our immune system, as well as that of many other advanced species, is composed of two subordinate immune systems (or immune responses): innate and adaptive systems. You can think of the innate immune system as the first layer of defense, while the adaptive immune system can be thought of as a more powerful follow-on defense layer that protects living species from harmful invaders.[173] The ability of the adaptive immune system to fend off external enemies is due to two factors that are also influenced by shape: specificity and memory. When a harmful foreign entity enters the bloodstream of a living organism, the adaptive immune system attempts to discover the shape of the invading body. As soon as the host recognizes that shape, the adaptive immune system begins to mercilessly attack the

---

173. Physical barriers such as the skin are usually considered to be the first layer of defense, and so the innate system becomes the second layer, while the adaptive system becomes the third.

foreign invaders by furiously replicating its defenses, which now match the invader's particular shape. The idea at work is perhaps similar to trying to discover the name of a stranger sitting next to you by uttering every name in existence while carefully observing which name the person responds to. This is what specificity is about. Memory, one the other hand, means that the organism "remembers" a particular shape and maintains a memory of it for future reference. Should the same foreign entity strike the host again, the host's immune system will immediately attack, and such an attack will be quite successful because the host already knows the invader's shape.

As you can see, shape's influence on so many (if not all) of the universe's constituents and its influence on so many of life's essential processes is rather profound. The Quran has captured this profundity in the following verse:

> *Our life giver [the god] is the one who gave everything its shape*
> *[or appearance], and then later provided its way [or purpose].*
> (20:50)

This verse clearly states that *shape* (*khalq*: "appearance, structure, shape, form") applies to *everything* (*kul'lu sha'i*) and that this shape is associated with a specific function or *purpose* (from *huda*: "guidance, direction, being shown the way"), aspects we are only beginning to understand and appreciate today. As was the case with precision, shape's importance could not have been fully understood or appreciated by those living fourteen hundred years ago, prior to the great many scientific advances that have enabled humans to discover and better understand the fascinating story of shape.

Epilogue

Well, we've come to the end of the ride, and I sincerely hope that it's been as informative and thought provoking as I promised it would be. There are, however, a few more important points I want to discuss before we bid each other a fond farewell and venture down the roads of our individual life journeys.

The first point relates to interpretation. Interpretation is clearly somewhat subjective, as multiple interpretations can be put forward for any given verse. If you ask a hundred knowledgeable native Arabic speakers to translate and interpret a particular verse, you will possibly end up with many different, sometimes conflicting, interpretations. This variability can be minimized or even eliminated, however, if there is common agreement to meaning and, more importantly, if there is *concrete knowledge* of what is being communicated. The important question thus becomes this (even more so in the case of science-related verses): Where must this concrete knowledge come from when attempting to interpret a science-related or natural-world verse?

Wherever possible, I believe this knowledge must come from the truth of established science, regardless of how difficult accepting that truth may be. As a matter of fact, I can argue that it's only through established science that many of the verses presented in this book can be properly understood or even made sense of. Thus, in addition to being linguistically valid and linguistically accurate, the book's interpretations communicate the Quran's scientific insights and some of its most profound meanings.

The second point relates to the degree to which I successfully argued agreement between science and the Quran for each of the thirty or so areas of science presented. You can certainly take any one of these areas and find a way to refute the claims of agreement between science and the Quran. For instance, it's possible, with reference to the verse on the expansion of the universe, that *sky* does not constitute "the universe" but a cloud or some other sky-related thing. After all, I myself pointed out several times throughout the book that the same words in the Quran can, and sometimes do, assume multiple distinct meanings. And if *sky* does not mean "the universe," then you do not have a verse that talks about the expansion of the universe (but then the verse makes little sense, if any at all). While it may be possible to challenge and refute a number of these verses on a case-by-case basis, I believe that what fails to materialize is a challenge and refutation of the sum of the science presented. In other words, we must recognize that something quite intriguing is going on here when we take a step back and look at this picture in its entirety. In the aggregate, the Quran provides overwhelming modern-day scientific insight.

The third point relates to the kind of science I consider worthy of being included in the book. The science-related verses I present here constitute a fraction of a larger set of science-related verses provided by the Quran. As stated previously, it's been estimated that the Quran contains more than 750 natural world verses, only some of which were presented in these pages. Why leave these out? Because I wanted this book to focus almost exclusively on aspects of the natural world that could not have been known fourteen hundred years ago. The Quran contains many verses that talk—accurately— about how rain forms through the coming together of "heavy" clouds; how hail forms through "mountainous" clouds (what we today refer to as tall cumulonimbus clouds); how bees produce "medicines" (honey is well known today for its antibacterial properties); how "barriers" exist between fresh and salt waters so that they do not mix together; how winds "fertil- ize" (plants); and how plants, like humans and animals, are also divided into male and female sexes, among numerous other science-related verses. However, none of these verses made their way into this book because I could not convince myself that these weren't aspects of the natural world that humans did not know when the Quran was first revealed. And as I said, I wanted this book to present science that was only discovered after the Quran had been fully revealed and that was only discovered within our very recent human history.

The last point I will make is the most important one and concerns the notion of proof. Within the sphere of science as well as that of pure math- ematics, proof takes on an important and privileged connotation. Prov- ing something requires much substantiation, overwhelming agreement, and—above all else—truth. Given that I used *proof* in the book's title—a decision I belabored for a while—can it be said that I met the minimum proof requirements that justify such use? I have endeavored my best to do so, but in the end, and in my mind at least, proof is about evidence and rationality, and this is no truer than when attempting to prove something as significant and elusive as that of the existence of a supreme being (let's not forget that rational thought *is* the foundation of Western science and philosophy). As such, I believe that I will have reached the aim of offering apt proof if an overwhelming majority of unbiased readers, after carefully examining the evidence presented and after employing a logical thought process, come to the conclusion that the book's central theme is a rational one, worthy of acceptance. If and when this happens, then I, hopefully along with the vast majority of readers, will consider the book's central theme to be plausibly proven.

It goes without saying, though, that I do not have any vested interest in the matter, and whether readers choose to accept the book's central theme or not, I remain indifferent to (and most likely completely unaware of) such a choice. My thrill along this ride comes from hoping that I have challenged and stimulated many a doubting and curious mind out there and, in the process, perhaps even managed to successfully contribute—only very slightly—to our own species' collective wisdom, enrichment, and happiness.

Bibliography

Arabic References

El-Albani, Muhammad Nassir-El-Deen. *Silsilet El-Ahadeeth El-Saheeha*. Riyadh, Saudi Arabia: The Maarif Library, 2007 (2nd printing).

El-Amidi El-Tamimi, Abdul-Wahid. *Hikkem El-Imam Ali Alaiyhee El-Salam: Aw Ghurer El-Hikkem We Durrer El-Kelim*. Beirut, Lebanon: Alaalami Library, 2002.

El-Mahili, Jalal El-Deen, and Jalal El-Deen El-Seuti. *Tafseer El-Jalalain*. Beirut, Lebanon: Dar Ehiaa Al-Torath Al-Arabi, 1999.

El-Sabouni, Muhammad Ali. *Safwat El-Tafaseer*, Vols. 1–3. Cairo, Egypt: Dar El-Sabouni Printing, 1977.

El-Shaarawi, Muhammad Metwelli. *Qisas El-Enbiaa Wel-Mursaleen*. Cairo, Egypt: El-Tawfeeqeeya Library, 2000.

El-Shirbini, Mahmud Ibrahim. *El-Ijaz El-Ilmi lil-Quran Fee Mejal Ulum El-Ardh*. Cairo, Egypt: Medbouli Library, 2010.

El-Tabtabaii, Muhammad Hussain. *El-Meezan Fee Tafseer El-Quran*, Vols. 1–22. Beirut, Lebanon: Al-Aalami Printers, 1997.

English References

Armstrong, Karen. *Islam: A Short History*. London: Phoenix Press, 2001.

Baalbaki, Rohi. *Al-Mawrid* (Arabic-English dictionary), 21st ed. Beirut, Lebanon: Dar El-Ilm Lilmalayin, 2007.

Barrow, John D. *New Theories of Everything*. New York: Oxford University Press, 2008.

Batchelor, John, and Christopher Chant. *The Complete Encyclopedia of Sailing Ships: 2000 BC–2006 AD*. Edison, NJ: Chartwell Books, 2006.

Cairns-Smith, A. G. *Seven Clues to the Origin of Life*. Cambridge, England: Cambridge University Press, 1985.

Cowan, J. M., ed. *The Hans Wehr Dictionary of Modern Written Arabic*. Urbana, IL: Spoken Language Services, 1994.

Cox, Brian, and Jeff Forshaw. *Why Does E=mc²?: (And Why Should We Care?)* Cambridge, MA: Da Capo Press, 2009.

Culver, Henry B. *The Book of Old Ships: From Egyptian Galleys to Clipper Ships*. Toronto, ONT: General Publishing, 1992.

Dantzig, Tobias. *Number: The Language of Science*. New York: Plume, 2007.

Dastjerdi, Hossein Vahid, Dr., trans. *Peak of Rhetoric: Maxims of the Holy Prophet Muhammad*. Qum: Ansariyan Publications, 2006.

Di Giulio, Massimo. "The Universal Ancestor Was a Thermophile or a Hyperthermophile." *Journal of Theoretical Biology* 221, no. 3 (2003): 425–36.

Dyson, Freeman. *Origins of Life*. Cambridge, England: Cambridge University Press, 1999.

Emerick, Yahiya. *The Life and Work of Muhammad*. Indianapolis, IN: Alpha Books, 2002.

Esack, Farid. *The Qur'an: A User's Guide*. Oxford, England: Oneworld Publications, 2005.

Farmelo, Graham. *It Must Be Beautiful: Great Equations of Modern Science*. London: Granta Books, 2003.

Feynman, Richard P. *The Character of Physical Law* (Messenger Lectures, 1964). Cambridge, MA: MIT Press, 1967.

Feynman, Richard P. *QED: The Strange Theory of Light and Matter*. Princeton, NJ: Princeton University Press, 1985.

Flannagan, Geraldine Lux. *Beginning Life: The Marvelous Journey from Conception to Birth*. Willowdale, ONT: Firefly Books, 1996.

Ford, Kenneth W. *The Quantum World: Quantum Physics for Everyone*. London: Harvard University Press, 2004.

Freely, John. *Aladdin's Lamp: How Greek Science Came to Europe through the Islamic World*. New York: First Vintage Books, 2010.

Gale, Joseph. *Astrobiology of Earth: The Emergence, Evolution, and Future of Life on a Planet in Turmoil*. New York: Oxford University Press, 2009.

Golshani, Mehdi. *The Holy Qur'an and the Sciences of Nature: A Theological Reflection*. New York: Global Scholarly Publications, 2003.

Gratzer, Walter. *Giant Molecules: From Nylon to Nanotubes*. Oxford: Oxford University Press, 2009.

Greene, Brian. *The Fabric of the Cosmos: Space, Time, and the Texture of Reality*. New York: First Vintage Books, 2005.

Griffin, Donald R. *Animal Minds*. Chicago: University of Chicago Press, 1992.

Gruendler, Beatrice. *The Development of the Arabic Scripts: From the Nabatean Era to the First Islamic Century According to Dated Texts*. Atlanta, GA: Scholar Press, 1993.

Guth, Alan H. *The Inflationary Universe: The Quest for a New Theory of Cosmic Origins*. New York: Basic Books, 1997.

Haylamaz, Resit. *Khadija: The First Muslim and the Wife of the Prophet Muhammad*. Somerset, NJ: Tughra Books, 2009.

Hazen, Robert. *Origins of Life*. The Teaching Company, Course 1515: The Great Courses, 2007. DVD, 12 hours.

Herbert, Nick. *Quantum Reality: Beyond the New Physics*. New York: Anchor Books, 1987.

Holldobler, Bert, and E. O. Wilson. *The Superorganism: The Beauty, Elegance, and Strangeness of Insect Societies*. New York: W. W. Norton & Company, 2009.

Jarosik, N., C. L. Bennett, J. Dunkley, B. Gold, M. R. Greason, M. Halpern, R. S. Hill, G. Hinshaw, et al. "Seven-Year Wilkinson Microwave Anisotropy Probe (WMAP) Observations: Sky Maps, Systematic Errors, and Basic Results." *The Astrophysical Journal Supplement*, Volume 192, Issue 2, article id. 14 (2011) (26 January, 2010). doi: 10.1088/0067-0049/192/2/14.

Johnston, Sean F. *History of Science*. Oxford: Oneworld Publications, 2009.

Kailani, Taiseer Zaid. *Modern Cosmology and the Quran: From a Scientific Perspective*. Bloomington, IN: AuthorHouse, 2005.

Khalidi, Tarif. *The Qur'an: Translated*. New York: Penguin Books, 2008.

Kiernan, Denise, and Joseph D'Agnese. *Science 101: Chemistry*. New York: HarperCollins Publishing, 2007.

Kirschner, Marc W., and John C. Gerhart. *The Plausibility of Life: Resolving Darwin's Dilemma*. New Haven, CT: Yale University Press, 2005.

Lane, Nick. *Life Ascending: The Ten Great Inventions of Evolution*. New York: W. W. Norton, 2009.

Laughlin, Robert B. *A Different Universe: Reinventing Physics from the Bottom Down*. Cambridge, MA: Basic Books, 2006.

Lederman, Leon, and Dick Teresi. *The God Particle: If the Universe Is the Answer, What Is the Question?* New York: First Mariner Books, 2006.

Lings, Martin. *Muhammad: His Life Based on the Earliest Sources*. Rochester, VT: Inner Traditions, 2006.

Lisi, A. Garrett, and James Owen Weatherall. "A Geometric Theory of Everything: Deep Down, the Particles and Forces of the Universe Are a Manifestation of Exquisite Geometry." *Scientific American* December (2010): 54–61.

Mathez, Edmond A., and James D. Webster. *The Earth Machine: The Science of a Dynamic Planet*. New York: Columbia University Press, 2004.

Mattson, Ingrid. *The Story of the Qur'an: Its History and Place in Muslim Life*. Malden, MA: Blackwell Publishing, 2008.

Moore, Keith L., and T. V. N. Persaud. *The Developing Human: Clinically Oriented Embryology*, 7th ed. Philadelphia: Elsevier Science, 2003.

Morgan, Michael Hamilton. *Lost History: The Enduring Legacy of Muslim Scientists, Thinkers, and Artists*. Washington, DC: National Geographic Society, 2007.

Morowitz, Harold J. *The Emergence of Everything: How the World Became Complex*. New York: Oxford University Press, 2002.

Murchie, Guy. *Music of the Spheres: The Material Universe—From Atom to Quasar, Simply Explained*. New York: Dover Books, 1967.

Noble, Denis. *The Music of Life: Biology beyond Genes*. Oxford, England: Oxford University Press, 2006.

NurBaki, Haluk. *Verses of Qur'an and Facts of Science*. Bombay, India: Bilal Books, 1997.

Pagels, Heinz R. *The Cosmic Code: Quantum Physics as the Language of Nature*. New York: Bantam Books, 1982.

Parekh, AbdulKarim. *Complete Easy Dictionary of the Qur'an*. Kuala Lumpur: A. S. Noordeen, 2010 (3rd printing).

Penrice, John. *A Dictionary and Glossary of the Qur'an*. Kuala Lumpur, Malaysia: The Other Press, 2006.

Razwy, Syed A. A. *Khadija-tul-Kubra (The Wife of the Prophet Muhammed)*. Elmhurst, NY: Tahrike Tarsile Quran, 1990.

Rees, Martin. *Just Six Numbers: The Deep Forces That Shape the Universe*. New York: Basic Books, 2000.

Regis, Ed. *What Is Life?: Investigating the Nature of Life in the Age of Synthetic Biology*. New York: Oxford University Press, 2008.

Rogers, Lesley J. *Minds of Their Own: Thinking and Awareness in Animals*. Boulder, CO: Westview Press, 1998.

Roston, Eric. *The Carbon Age: How Life's Core Element Has Become Civilization's Greatest Threat*. New York: Walker Publishing Company, 2008.

Sagan, Carl. *Cosmos*. New York: Random House, 1983.

Sarton, George. *From Homer to Omar Khayyam*, Vol. 1, *Introduction to the History of Science*. Baltimore: The Williams & Wilkins Co., 1927.

Schopt, J. William. *Life's Origin: The Beginnings of Biological Evolution*. Berkeley: University of California Press, 2002.

Seife, Charles. *Decoding the Universe: How the New Science of Information is Explaining Everything in the Cosmos, From our Brains to Black Holes*. New York: Penguin Group, 2006.

Southwood, Richard. *The Story of Life*. New York: Oxford University Press, 2004.

Stannard, Russell. *The End of Discovery: Are We Approaching the Boundaries of the Knowable?* New York: Oxford University Press, 2010.

Sternberg, Robert J. *Wisdom: Its Nature, Origins, and Development*. Cambridge, England: Cambridge University Press, 1990.

Stewart, Ian. *The Story of Mathematics: From Babylonian Numerals to Chaos Theory*. London: Quercus, 2008.

Strathern, Paul. *Mendeleyev's Dream: The Quest for the Elements*. New York: Berkley Books, 2000.

Tarbuck, Edward J., and Frederick K. Lutgens. *Earth: An Introduction to Physical Geology*, 9th ed. Upper Saddle River, NJ: Pearson Prentice Hall, 2008.

Thomas, Lewis. *The Medusa and the Snail: More Notes of a Biology Watcher*. New York: Penguin Books, 1995.

Tyson, Neil DeGrasse, and Donald Goldsmith. *Origins: Fourteen Billion Years of Cosmic Evolution*. New York: W. W. Norton, 2005.

Vedral, Vlatko. *Decoding Reality: The Universe as Quantum Information*. New York: Oxford University Press, 2010.

Vertosick, Frank T. *The Genius Within: Discovering the Intelligence of Every Living Thing*. Orlando, FL: Harcourt Books, 2002.

Von Denffer, Ahmad. *Ulum al-Quran: An Introduction to the Sciences of the Quran*. Leicestershire, United Kingdom: The Islamic Foundation, 1983.

Ward, Peter D., and Donald Brownlee. *Rare Earth: Why Complex Life Is Uncommon in the Universe*. New York: Copernicus Books, 2004.

Weiss, Kenneth M., and Anne V. Buchanan. *The Mermaid's Tale: Four Billion Years of Cooperation in the Making of Living Things*. London: Harvard University Press, 2009.

Wolpert, Lewis. *How We Live & Why We Die: The Secret Lives of Cells*. New York: W. W. Norton, 2009.

Woodman, Richard. *The History of the Ship: The Comprehensive Story of Seafaring from the Earliest Times to the Present Day*. London: Second Lyons Press, 2002.

Yahya, Harun. *Miracles of the Qur'an*. Scarborough, ONT: Al-Attique Publishers, 2001.

Yau, Shing-Tung, and Steve Nadis. *The Shape of Inner Space: String Theory and the Geometry of the Universe's Hidden Dimensions*. New York: Basic Books, 2010.

Index